Passing Through The Fever:

Anatomy of an Epidemic

Sawchuk, L.A.
Benady, S.G.
Burke S.D.A.

Published by Diva Media,
Toronto

© Diva Media 2005
First Published 2005

ISBN 0-9738794-0-8

Toronto 2005

For Sarita Benady

Contents

Acknowledgements

We wish to thank the Wellcome Library, London, for their generous permission to publish William Thornton's Diary, which forms the cornerstone of this work. S. Chan, A. Daust, K. Denny, J. Ruby, J. Padiak and other students - all deserve thanks for their artwork. Ken Jones (UTSC) and Paul Balban (Gibraltar) assisted by providing the photographs. A special note of appreciation is given to the Public Record Office (PRO), Gibraltar Museum (GM), Gibraltar Archives (GA), Marrache Foundation Trust - sketches from Major General Henry Sandham (hereafter MFT), Garrison Library (GL) and Tito Benady for allowing us to gain access to a number of illustrations used in this book. We are extremely grateful to Clive and Geraldine Finlayson who allowed us to modify an earlier version of this book – Diary of an Epidemic published by the Gibraltar Government Heritage Publications Monographs 3. Their support allowed us to initiate this new project and their support for us has been unwavering.

Candace Lee, a recent graduate in New Media Studies at the University of Toronto at Scarborough, put the book together in its present fashion using InDesign. We thank her for her patience, creativity and great sense of humour working with one of us (L.A.S.). Also, we would like to thank Dayna Boyer, the copyeditor, who took our words and transformed them into a much more readable text. All errors and omissions are the responsibility of L.A.S.

The funding for trips to London and Gibraltar came largely from the Social Sciences and Humanities Research Council of Canada.

Finally, a special thanks to the staff, Gail Copland and Audrey Glasbergen, and to John Miron, the Chair of the Departement of Social Sciences, University of Toronto for supporting this project. Their encouragement in the publication of this book is warmly appreciated by the authors.

GIBRALTARIAN WOMAN (GM)

<h1 style="text-align: center;">–1–</h1>

The Epidemic Experience

SPANISH GUARDS AT THE FRONTIER

Introduction

It was late summer of the year 1828. Within the high, cold stone walls of the city, a great fever was raging. As the sun slowly started to emerge from the blazing, golden horizon behind the stark grey cliff of the North Front, 18 year old Amelia Rowley set off to see her fiancé, Esteban Balban. Amelia's family had moved to Gibraltar from England because her father had obtained a position as an engineer on the Rock. Amelia was 16 at the time, and not long af-

ter the move she met Esteban in the local market. Though Amelia could not speak Spanish, Esteban's English was good enough that a courtship soon blossomed. Esteban lived across the border in the neighbouring Spanish town of San Roque. In her finest Sunday clothes, Amelia paced the ground waiting for the fortress gates to open. They were supposed to be opened at dawn, but the guards were often late, and Amelia fretted with impatience. Just the night before, she had received the awful news from a neighbour that spurred her into

GIBRALTARIAN LADY (GM)

frenzy. Amelia learned that her lover Esteban had been drafted into the Spanish Army. Knowing that she most likely would not see him again for at least three years - if he survived that long - Amelia set off that morning with great trepidation, hoping to see him one more time, and praying that it would not be the last time that she ever saw Esteban. Like all the travelers wishing to enter Spain during the fever period, she stood patiently in the hot sun waiting for her turn to cross the border. When she finally arrived at the sentry post, after hours of waiting, her heart started to pound with great excitement, for she could just barely see Esteban through the bars. He was waiting! – she was a mere 10 meters from the tender embrace she longed for. The guard's rough voice sliced through her thoughts: "Su pase de la fiebre, Señorita!"[1] Amelia looked confused; she had not understood a word, and all she *could think was, "I may never see him again." The guard growled out once more with even greater urgency: "Su pase ahora!"[2] Still Amelia did not understand him, but she sensed there was a problem. She couldn't risk being turned back. Feeling that she had no choice, she slipped past the guard and ran across the border as fast as her bare feet could take her. Everything became a blur; she could only see Esteban's face. Suddenly a shot rang out, and seemed to echo back and forth as if it would never cease. Amelia stumbled and collapsed, only a few feet from Esteban. As he ran forward aghast and picked up his fiancée's limp body, he could see blood pouring out of a wound in her chest. The musket shot had ripped through her small body. As Amelia took her last breath, Esteban, with tears in his eyes, took one last look at his fiancée alive.*

The above fictional account speaks to an often-overlooked fact of life during an epidemic, that outbreaks are much more than a biological encounter with disease. In this case, a person without proof of having 'passed through the fever' puts every individual in harm's way, not from the disease per se but from harsh draconian restrictions imposed by distant authorities. In epidemic times, the pen held by such an official who sat behind a desk thousands of miles away could instantly take away everyday civil rights. In their dark musty offices, officials issued proclamations that controlled and limited freedoms people once took for granted – the freedom to travel, their ability to buy and sell the food necessary for sustenance, and their livelihood. As the text unfolds, it will become clear that past, present, or future outbreaks are not merely biologically-driven events, but rather, complex organic phenomena that cannot simply be captured by an examination of the pathogen, statistical practices, and a week in some foreign setting.

Generalizations on Epidemics

Over the course of human history, the specter of misery, illness, and death at the hands of epidemics has shaped the human condition. The need for a greater understanding of the impact of disease on communities is grounded in the unfortunate fact that epidemics have, and continue to, decimate populations, paralyze industry and trade, and cause human despair. Understanding how one population and its various citizens responded to a major epidemic could be instructive for today's society, which is increasingly forced to deal with old and new contagions. For the history student, an epidemic can also be an invaluable research tool, shedding light onto the fabric of societies long since past. Here, a community's experience with an epidemic can provide a window through which the researcher can peer into the interplay of a society's economic, political, and social processes. It is also during times of great stress and dislocation that medical thought and sanitary thinking are brilliantly illuminated and revolutionized. A decade ago Daniel Fox put forth "a few cautious generalizations" regarding outbreaks in past populations and what one should expect under epidemic conditions:

> At the beginning of most epidemics, many people, including many in medicine and politics, have underestimated the severity of the problem.
>
> Considerable fear and anxiety has accompanied the perception that an epidemic was gaining strength.
>
> Initial responses to fear and anxiety have included flight, denial, and scapegoating of alleged carriers of the disease -- notably foreigners.
>
> Efforts to quarantine (separate people who may carry the disease) and isolate (set apart people with the disease) have usually been ineffective in limiting the spread of an epidemic.

After a period of denial or of panic, rational policies have been established during each epidemic, almost always by a coalition of business and government leaders, with support from prominent members of the medical profession.

In most epidemics there have been shortages of physicians and nurses to treat the sick poor. Shortages of physicians have almost always been met by providing incentives, usually money and future practice opportunities, to physicians of lower status, often from another city or foreign country.

Epidemics are always expensive. They have exacted a heavy toll in direct costs (treatment and public health measures) and indirect costs (losses of productivity, especially of lifetime earnings). That burden has always been borne by government and philanthropy as well as by private individuals.

While Fox's statements are useful descriptive generalizations, other scholars have gone further to develop theoretical paradigms allowing us a different sort of perspective to understand and compare populations undergoing changes triggered by crisis mortality. Viewed from the perspective of the vast antiquity of human history, populations have gone through a series of transitions, often mirrored by changes in the magnitude and patterning of mortality profiles and the predominant causes of death shaping those profiles. Depending on a complex system of social, economic, ecological, and biological factors unique to each community, the state of mortality remains relatively stable over time. This equilibrium, however, is greatly disturbed by moments of crisis such as famine, war, floods, or epidemics. Local epidemics, and their wider global counterparts, pandemics, strike a community hard. In so doing, they create unusual opportunities for rapid population turnover, profound social change, and even long-term evolutionary transformation. Numerous scholars have tried to capture the nature and trajectory of this demographic transition and accompanying moments of crisis mortality in theoretical terms that are grounded either in broad historical trends or in epidemiological principles.

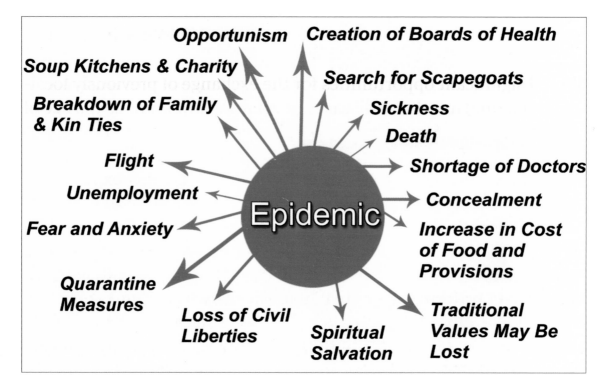

FIGURE 1. CONSEQUENCES OF AN EPIDEMIC

One of the earliest explanatory models, put forth by William McNeill (1976), posited four major transitions in the disease history of human populations that began with the move towards a sedentary lifestyle. The first stage began about 10, 000 to 5, 000 years ago, as sedentary human groups began to turn to domestication. Exposure to new microbes originated from this new lifestyle which involved closer contact with domesticated animals as well as other microbes potentially carried by the 'pest' species (e.g. rats, mice, flies). These pest species are naturally attracted to the accumulations of people, food, and waste products which are typical of stationary populations. As sedentary human populations began to grow in size and density, they also expanded spatially and grew in social complexity. Within this context, state-level societies and empires (a merging of previously distinct state societies) followed. The second transition posits that the intermingling of large and powerful Eurasian civilizations – in trade and war – beginning about 3,000 to 1,500 years ago, offered significant opportunities for the exchange of previously localized (endemic) infectious diseases in what we now know as the age of famine, pestilence, and plague. Within this context, important population-level differences in susceptibility to infectious diseases began to manifest – those populations with longer histories of exposure or more intense exposure to given infectious diseases possessed greater potential genetic or immunologic resistance to those diseases. Devastation typically followed when infectious diseases were introduced to a population for the first time and everyone was equally susceptible (that is, a virgin soil population). The third transition takes place during the time of European exploration, expansion, and colonization, beginning about 1500 AD and continuing over approximately five centuries. When colonizers entered new populations, there was a meeting between the settlers and the indigenous people of that community, and consequently a meeting between groups with, entirely different disease histories and exposures. It is within this framework, for example, that we begin to understand the devastation that accompanied first contacts between the "Old World" (Africa, Asia, Europe) and the "New World" (the Americas) (see Dobson, 1989). The fourth transition considers global population and disease-dynamics that are taking place today, in a world that has seemingly become much smaller through innovations in technology – particularly the airplane.

On the other hand, the epidemiological transition theory put forth by also retains the element of stages but focuses less on a precise historical timetable and more on the nature of shifting disease patterns[3]. The first stage, *'the age of pestilence and famine'*, is marked by: high death and birth rates, wide swings in mortality, little population growth with very low life expectancy, and a high prevalence of infectious disease. The second stage, *'the age of receding pandemics'*, is characterized by a decreasing prevalence of infectious disease, declining fertility and overall mortality, and a slow rise in the occurrences of chronic degenerative diseases. In the third stage, *'the age of degenerative and man-made disease'*, the category of infectious disease becomes rare. During this stage, chronic degenerative and stress-related diseases become the primary cause of death. The population structure of the third stage consists of a lower proportion of younger people relative to elderly citizens. A key feature of the epidemiological transition theory is the connection between modernization, socioeconomic progress, and mortality decline via changing epidemiologic conditions. Since this theory offers a broad explanatory framework, the model has been applied to numerous populations to explain the observed mortality patterns (see, for example, Cook & Dummer, 2004; Garcia-Moro et al., 2000).

This text recognizes the value of both paradigms, but openly accepts the criticisms of others found in both theories (Gaylin & Kates, 1997; Carolina & Gustavo, 2003; Barrett, Kuzawa, McDade, & Armelagos, 1998; Waters, 2001). First, the shift in a population's demographic state should not be seen as entering a precise stage or phase at particular times but rather, a population in dynamic flux that defies easy taxonomic phases. Further, it is unlikely that all populations underwent this transition in a uniform manner moving in a purely simple and deterministic fashion. In addition, the change in a community is unlikely to be uniform since changes occur at different rates depending on the nature of the groups within the population, be it class, gender, or other variants. Finally, while each of the models focuses on mortality per se, comparatively little attention is given to changes in well-being and the quality of life (Seale, 2000).

The Case Study Approach and Investigating Epidemics

The grounding for this work lies in the case study methodology. While there are discipline-based variations inherent to the case study approach (see for example Tellis 1997), there are a number of common attributes that collectively illustrate the defining elements of this type of investigation. First, the fundamental unit of study is the community. Using this particular research design the vexing problems of sampling and representativeness are avoided. Another quality is community familiarity, a quality that can only be gained from long-term commitment by the investigator[4]. A further salient feature of the case study approach is that it is both holistic as well as ingrained in nature[5]. A fourth element is a constellation of special qualities that mark the uniqueness of the community itself as a 'living laboratory' for scientific research. Here, the community should be ideally self-defined and spatially-bounded so that all can agree on what constitutes and defines the community. Another essential attribute of the case study approach is the incorporation of multiple perspectives. This means that a researcher considers not just the 'voice' and perspective of the inhabitants, but also that of various social groups, and the interaction between them[6]. Fundamental to the case study approach is that multiple and independent sources of information are used to ensure desirable qualities of validity, reliability, and consistency[7]. Finally, while it may be difficult to make broad generalizations from a single study[8],

9

the case study design can be used to verify or question an existing paradigm, or to represent an unusual situation that may provide unique insights into the dynamics of a population with epidemic disease.

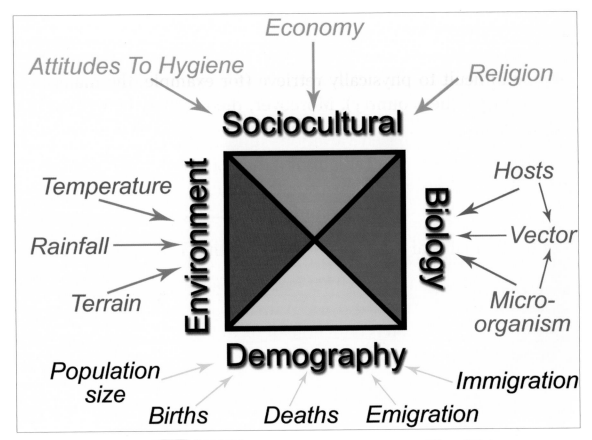

FIGURE 2. HOLISTIC MODEL OF COMMUNITY HEALTH

Sources of Information on Epidemics

In the study of historic epidemics, primary sources of information are necessarily retrospective and archival in nature. The strengths of archival sources are varied; first, the information is stable in that it can be viewed repeatedly over time as well as verified by different scholars. Second, archival material does not infringe on personal rights as documents are given access only after they have reached a specific time period (for example a census typically can be only made public after 100 years). Third, it is broad in temporal scope, often covering generations of changing knowledge on a subject. Despite these advantages, there are a number of potential weaknesses that must be recognized and acknowledged in any study. First, the necessary documentation may be difficult to physically retrieve (for example, the material is located in another country). Moreover, the text may be written in a foreign language and subject to issues of translation and misinterpretation. Thirdly, the quality of the remaining material may be fragmentary, damaged and difficult to read. Furthermore, the process of describing the epidemic disease may be vague or there may be no consensus regarding the name and causation of the disease itself. Access to the material may also be limited (that is, in private hands), and not readily available to the public. Most important amongst these limitations is the problem of biased selectivity where material only reflects a single point of view.

Challenged with these difficulties, researchers often turn opportunistically to a myriad of archival sources. The historical record itself is replete with possibilities: government records and correspondence, personal sources -- such as letters, obituaries, and diaries, medical sources which include books and journals as well as personal documents. Also, literary works by popular writers of the time provide a type of historical record, especially those writers who reflected on what was taking place in the world around them (whether it be fictional or non-fictional). As with any written materials, all of these sources must be critically evaluated, noting not only who wrote the material, but who they were writing it to/for, and why, ascertaining any particular underlying agenda which might influence their senti-

ABOVE: PRIMARY TEXT MATERIAL ON GIBRALTAR

List of the Inhabitants of Gibraltar, taken by General Boyd's Orders in February 1777.

			Total.
British or Protestant Inhabitants {	Natives	220	506.
	Not Natives	286	
Roman Catholic Inhabitants {	English and Irish	13	1832.
	Minorkeens	62	
	Natives	845	
	Genoese & Savoyards	672	
	Portugueze	93	
	Spaniards	134	
	French	13	
Jews {	Natives	696	863.
	Strangers	267	
		Total...	3201.

ments in writing. The issue of representativeness is another critical feature influencing the interpretation of written material and here, a staggeringly large number of issues must be considered. Most texts, for example, were written by the educated, middle to upper class – sometimes they wrote about their own issues and concerns, but they also wrote about the poor. In contrast, there are far fewer documents surviving which the poor wrote themselves. Unpopular views, or those not favoured by the political or social majority, may have been 'silenced' or unfairly represented in the written record.

Human Populations as Living Laboratories

In modern clinical investigations of disease etiology or causation, researchers go to great length in their inquiry to control for the differences that exist between their carefully selected groups. This is so that the units under study are as homogenous as possible in their attributes before comparing differences in sickness or mortality rates. The differences in exposure factors that remain are usually limited in number, highly recognizable, and can be methodologically operationalized by the researcher in the sterile lab setting. In stark contrast to this reductionist approach, investigators interested in the mortality experience at the community level are beset by a myriad of qualities that are far more complex and ethically impossible to control in real-world situations. Given the marked differences in approach, researchers wishing to undertake population-based retrospective studies search for naturally-occurring unique communities that have attributes that set them apart from most other human populations, while, at the same time, still experiencing the same epidemics that plagued the rest of humankind. For example, a community that has marked religious diversity provides an excellent opportunity to examine how differences in diet, food preparation, attitudes towards medical care, and so forth can affect the disease experience when a disease like cholera entered the community. In another example, researchers may choose to focus on a community that is primarily rural and basic in its subsistence pattern. Such a setting would limit the diversity of risk factors stemming from lifestyle, diet, and activity patterns. Taking advantage of the natural confluence of social, biological, and ecological factors that set a community apart from others is a strategy now being employed by the new scholars of epidemic research.

The Potential for High Background Mortality

Like many seaports around the world, early nineteenth century Gibraltar was an important port-of-call for both merchant ships and war vessels. With its free port status and strategic location, Gibraltar -- known colloquially as 'the Rock' -- served as a major node in a trade network that linked numerous centres throughout Europe, the Mediterranean, Africa, and the Americas into a vast reservoir of potential hosts for infectious disease. Through trade, colonialism, and militarism, the movement of people and goods efficiently and effectively influenced the emergence of a global pattern of disease transmission. As McNeil astutely observed decades ago:

> .... within such well-traveled waters as the Mediterranean, movement by seas could, with favorable winds, attain an average of well over 100 miles per day. Thus, all the coastal cities of the Mediterranean constituted a single disease pool. A person seemingly in good health at the time of embarkation might fall sick en route and communicate his illness to others on board. Shipboard travel could therefore easily carry an infection from one port to another, across hundreds or thousands of miles of water[9].

As a military post, the Gibraltar garrison held several thousand men as well as a small number of married soldiers' wives and families. In addition to those who were posted in Gibraltar for periods of up to two years, there were those in transit from all parts of the Empire whose stay in Gibraltar was limited to days. The movement of military personnel in large numbers grouped together and moving rapidly from place to place provided the ideal medium for the spread of infectious diseases. Then there was the daily movement of foreigners to the Rock, trying to sell their wares and produce or to seek work as labourers and servants. Thousands streamed through Gibraltar's gates daily. This co-mingling of men and women from near and far, with an already overcrowded and densely packed population, presented ideal conditions for the introduction and spread of both old and new infectious diseases. In a time that saw the mass movement of people and goods over vast distances within weeks, the global pattern of disease transmission was no longer in its infancy. Owing to the Rock's unusual configuration[10] as a port city, naval base, garrison town, and commercial centre, its residents would pay a high price, in terms of their health, for the town's participation in that global network.

This deadly potential accumulated greater strength as Gibraltar's inhabitants poured into limited livable space, straining the territory's primitive sanitary and healthcare infrastructure well past tolerable limits. It would be no exaggeration to state that Gibraltar, during the early decades of 19th century, achieved the dubious reputation as "a population, filthy in themselves, and overcrowded, perhaps, beyond any community in the world." Numerous factors collided to create this distinction; in the first place[11], population growth occurred at an unprecedented rate, with an infrastructure that was woefully inadequate to meet the demands of a sizeable population. Growth simply overwhelmed the available space and resources. This population overload was also aggravated by the fact that the landowners were more concerned with making large, quick profits than with providing proper accommodation for the impoverished working-class. Most of the poor lived in the up- per portions of the Rock, so the great "evils" of their existence were literally hidden from public view. While the upper echelons of Gibraltar's military were served quite well, living conditions for the rank and file were little better than for the civilians. Another factor that contributed to Gibraltar's abysmal living conditions was the lack of understand-

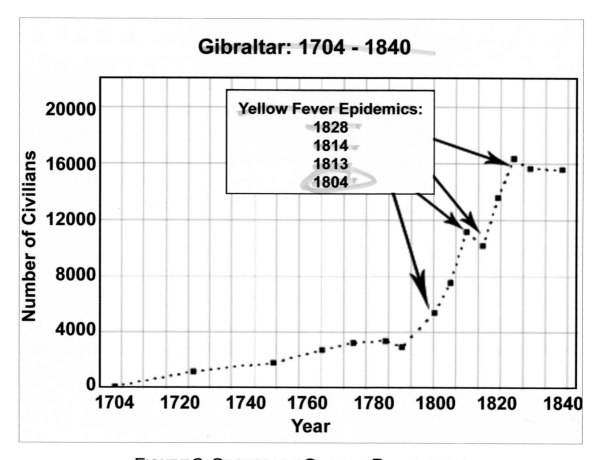

FIGURE 3. GROWTH OF CIVILIAN POPULATION

ing of the dangers of poor sanitation and the relation to health problems. However, even those armed with that knowledge were faced with a general reluctance on the part of the merchants and negligent landowners to pay higher taxes for questionable sanitary reforms. Further, there was at this time, no broad-based civilian body willing to, or capable of, enforcing improvements to Gibraltar's housing and sanitary infrastructure. And those few with both the knowledge and the will to introd
uce sanitary reform were rendered impotent by the fact that Gibraltar's civilian population was living within a military fortress with virtually no civil rights, and without the means of introducing any significant legislation.

The temporal focus of this work is a period when epidemic yellow fever peaked, marking the onset of Gibraltar's 'dark times' with dramatic episodes of crisis mortality[12]. It was during this period that deadly visitations of 'yellow jack'[13] spawned fear, havoc, and economic disruption, irreversibly tearing away at the very social foundation of the community. The first of these crises occurred in 1804 when yellow fever silently slipped through Gibraltar's guarded gates; within days cries of pain and agony could be heard in the crowded streets and dirty lanes of the garrison town. Ignorant of the nature and cause of yellow fever, the disease spread rapidly throughout the population of 15 000. Within weeks over 5000 perished at the hands of the dreaded black vomit fever. Gibraltar's 1804 epidemic was not a singular event but one of many outbreaks that devastated the lower Iberian peninsula; collectively, it was estimated that more than 50,000 died at the hands of yellow fever. The pattern of yellow fever outbreaks in towns and cities across Portugal, Spain, and Gibraltar provide stark evidence of just how interconnected communities were at this time

A MAP OF GIBRALTAR AND THE SURROUNDING COUNTRYSIDE (FROM WALSH, 1803)

ety of deadly contagions (both local and global diseases alike).

The re-emergence of yellow fever in 1828 in Gibraltar provides a telling example of the global redistribution of new and deadly organisms. The fury of the pathogen was dramatic, killing within just months one--tenth of all the residents. Those who survived were granted life-long immunity against this hemorrhagic fever, as well as memories of great loss and suffering. The objective of this work is to explore the reaction, impact, and consequences of this deadly scourge on multiple planes – those that touch on personal loss and grief to ones that capture the sweeping actions of nation states in the time of crisis. When viewed in its entirety, this work will draw the reader into such diverse domains as historicity (situating the epidemic in place and time), medical history (understanding how the epidemic was viewed 'then'), and epidemiology (understanding the origin and development of an epidemic using contemporary knowledge of yellow fever)[14]. To accomplish such lofty goals, we will use the diary of a resident, William Thornton, a local businessman, as one the cornerstones of this work. The daily flow of events chronicled in the diary chart the misery, fear, and untimely death associated with this epidemic disease[15].

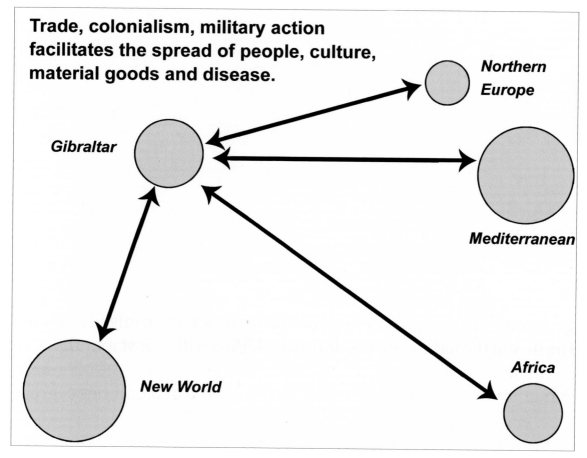

FIGURE 4. GIBRALTAR IN THE GLOBAL NETWORK OF COMMUNITIES

BACK FROM CONVENT GATE (MFT)

PLAZA SPANISH CHURCH (MFT)

COURTHOUSE (MFT)

SPANISH CHURCH IN THE BACKGROUND (MFT)

Gibraltar

Of Place

During the early 19th century, Gibraltar's burgeoning population was unevenly distributed among four distinct geographic spaces: the Town, the South, the North Front, and Catalan Bay. The Town was by far the most important, since it contained the commercial district and the bulk of the population. The locals called it the Town, ... though it was never spoken of as a City with "the second appellative ... [used] more frequently ... than the first."[16] Nestled on the western slope of the Rock, the Town consisted of two principal streets of parallel importance: Waterport Street housed shops and retail stores, and Irish Town, where wholesale and merchant stores were located. Much of the lower part of the Town was built on a strip of comparatively flat ground between the steep slope of the rock and the line wall that stretched from 12 to 20 feet above the high water mark. The remainder was built chiefly on the slope's terraces, one over the other, rising to an elevation of 250 feet above sea level.

From a distance, the panorama of the Town from on board a ship was described in more charitable terms, as "small crowded edifices, looking like card-houses, pasted to the naked rock, and so slight, as though swoop of the storm could scatter them upon the waves."[17] As for the architecture of the city itself, many of the buildings gave the visitor "an impression of fustiness, of backwatered Victorianism, of the shabby-genteel, and unjustified pretentiousness."[18] What was not in the hands of the military engineers was often left up to the builders, giving the place a very heterogeneous appearance. Gibraltar's vernacular architecture includes among its features "Georgian timber sash windows, Genoese louvered shutters, Regency cast iron balconies, Andalusian pantile roofs, flat roofs a la catalana, and keystones and arched doorways reminiscent of those in military buildings of the Ordnance...."[19]

Conditions on the upper slopes of the Rock,[20] which housed the poor and working classes, were particularly abysmal. There was an exorbitant amount of overcrowding and little in the way of amenities. The norm was as follows:

> The town of Gibraltar is in summer excessively close and oppressive, and at no time can it be, we should imagine, an agreeable place of residence; for not only are its habitations confusedly huddled together, but for the most part exceedingly ill-built and unsuitable to the climate. The rent of these uncomfortable habitations is also enormously dear.[21]

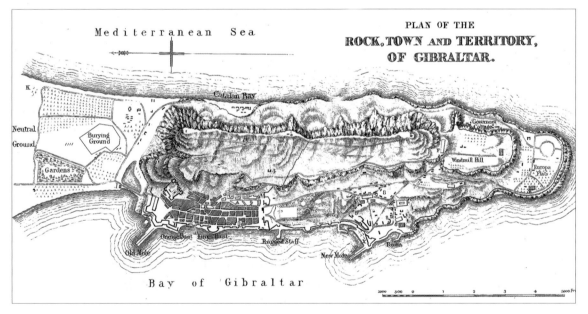

A MAP OF THE TERRITORY OF GIBRALTAR

(SAYER)

Much of the lower part of the Town had to be rebuilt after The Great Siege (1779-1783). The infrastructure plan for the upper part of the

Scene of destruction after Great Siege

Town was constrained by the topography of the very steep ground and curving hills. Since the old foundation, street pattern, and defense walls added extra planning limitations, the result was a maze of steps and alleyways [interspersed throughout the city][22]. Portrayals of life on the Rock throughout the 18th and 19th centuries would invariably refer to the recurring problems of the high cost of living, and the lack of affordable, decent accommodation -- particularly for the working class population.

In contrast to the high density living characteristic of the Town of Gibraltar was the largely uninhabited region known as the South. Called by some, "Gibraltar's second town,"[23] the South occupied most of the

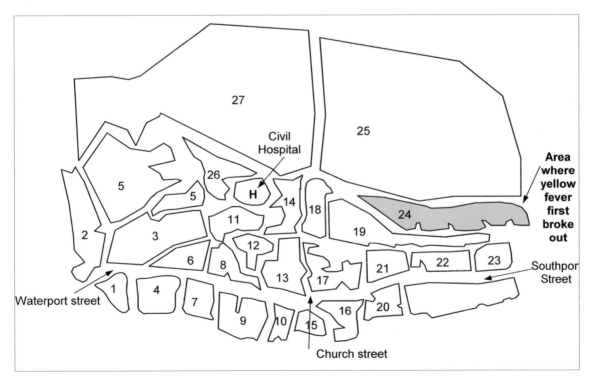

POLICE DISTRICTS IN THE TOWN OF GIBRALTAR

southern portion of the territory, a little over one square mile. Here,

ABOVE: OUTSIDE SOUTHPORT GATES (T. BENADY)

BELOW: COMMERCIAL SQUARE (T. BENADY)

THE ROMAN CATHOLIC CHURCH

ALAMEDA GARDENS

(T. BENADY)

a small civilian population, as well as a substantial military presence could be found scattered throughout the rocky landscape. Overall, the South was far less crowded than the Town proper; nonetheless, some districts were heavily populated. A housing survey, taken in 1816, revealed that only 48 houses were located in the South. Generally speaking, the sewers and house drains were considered to be extremely inadequate and poorly constructed.

A VIEW OF THE NEUTRAL GROUND

(MODIFIED FROM THE ILLUSTRATED LONDON NEWS, 1876)

Gibraltar's North Front consisted of a narrow neck of low-lying land, about three meters above sea level. It extended from the sheer north face of the Rock for about 800 meters beyond the frontier of the British lines towards the Spanish mainland. Given the salubrious nature of this sandy isthmus, the North Front was regarded at the turn of the 19th century as a healthy place. In fact, it was the place that individuals retreated to if they had not "passed through the epidemic."[25] A small population of a few hundred reportedly took up residence in small wooden huts erected on the sandy plain in the early 19th century. The residents of this temporary village were only permitted to remain there on sufferance.

THE FISHING VILLAGE OF CATALAN BAY

On the eastern coast of Gibraltar was the small, isolated community of Catalan Bay. This small fishing village was permanently established shortly after 1787[26]. Given limited space and military concerns, the right to residence and the settlement's size were strictly monitored and regulated[27]. In addition to the small civilian population, Catalan Bay had barracks for about 10 officers and 50 men. During the formative period of settlement, the principal inhabitants were Genoese. The men were primarily engaged in fishing. During the epidemic of 1828, the village consisted of about 80 houses.

The Spanish area immediately adjacent to Gibraltar was called the Campo area, and it consisted of a number of villages in close proximity to Gibraltar (see Table 1). These villages provided day-workers, food, and other necessary provisions for the Garrison when Spain was not hostile to its Gibraltarian neighbours.

Spanish Locations/Towns	Distance form Gibraltar (Miles)	Population Size
Spanish troops at the Lines	1.25	3,000
San Roque	5	6,000
Algeciras	11	9,000-14,000
Los Barrios	15.5	1,500

TABLE 1. SPANISH TOWNS CA 1828
(HENNEN 1830: PAGE 106)

The Civilian Inhabitants

At the time of the fever epidemics, Gibraltar was a truly cosmopolitan centre – rich in both people and cultures (see Table 2). Much of Gibraltar's civilian population consisted of the working poor – individuals who lived from day-to-day performing basic, unskilled labour. There was also a small minority of bourgeois and upper class citizens – the merchants and landowners. Between these two widely disparate groups, there was a moderately sized group of small-scale traders, contractors, and civil ser-

GIBRALTAR'S INHABITANTS

(J. RUBY)

Depictions of Some of the Inhabitants of Gibraltar

vants that benefited from the commercial activities of the town, as well as from the presence of a large garrison stationed on the Rock. In addition to a native-born civilian or 'fixed population', there was a

Nation	Males		Females		Total
	Above 12 yrs	Under 12 yrs	Above 12 yrs	Under 12 yrs	
British Subjects	399	86	390	90	965
Native Christians	1,293	2,065	1,583	1,967	6,905
Native Jews	379	234	409	278	1300
Barbary Jews	381	14	46	5	446
Brazilians	4	2	3	1	10
French	46		20		66
Genoese	940	93	411	88	1,532
Germans	56	22	10		66
Italians	127	2	34	10	193
Moors	11	35	1	4	18
Portuguese	570		283	22	910
Prussians	3		1		4
Russians	1		2		3
Spaniards	1,492	189	2,064	181	3,926
South America	10	1	5		16
Swedes	2		1		3
Swiss	5		1		6
Turks	12				12
United States of America	5	1	5	2	10
Total	5,736	2,744	5,266	2,648	16,394

TABLE 2. CIVILIAN POPULATION OF GIBRALTAR, MARCH 6TH 1829

LA PLAZA (MFT)

demographically and socially significant group known to the colonial officials as the 'floating' or 'alien' population. Gibraltar was largely dependent upon this large non-British foreign-born population element for its workforce. While not technically a "community" per se, aliens did participate in virtually all aspects of daily life in Gibraltar, at least until an epidemic struck and movement in and out of the garrison came to a complete halt.

Given its strategic location, it is not surprising that 19th century Gibraltar was rich in peoples and their material cultures. The diverse character of the inhabitants of the Rock could be seen not only in dress, but also in dietary preferences. One early traveler astutely observed:

> Neither do the inhabitants confine their national partiality to dress alone: they let it follow them home; and give it a place at the table and the hearth. In one house, children are brought up on Neapolitan macaroni; in the next, the cry is for "bannocks of bear-meal, bannocks of barley!" Here, you may hear unleavened bread called for in Hebrew, during the Passover; and at the opposite door, the Irish name for potatoes every day in the year.[29]

These remarks also illustrate another telling feature of life in Gibraltar: the experience of communal patio living. Residence within multi-family buildings and the sharing of resources brought people of various nationalities in close proximity to one another; this, in turn, contributed to a high degree of tolerance and respect for ethnic and religious diversity among residents of the Rock. Early travelers also keenly observed a growing sense of self-identification. By the early 19th century, native-born inhabitants no longer maintained a social reference to the country of their parents, but came to think of themselves as 'Rock Scorpions'.[30]

TWO PORTERS AT WORK IN GIBRALTAR

(FROM A WATERCOLOUR BY STAUNTON ST. CLAIR, GM)

The Military and Colonial Officials

A significant component of the population resident in Gibraltar was made up of the military, whose presence loomed large not only because it was numerically substantial but also because it possessed a certain social and psychological weight over the civilians. While military strength in Gibraltar during the early 19th century varied from year to year,[31] the resident military population, including women and children, typically made up about one quarter of the total number of inhabitants. At the start of the 1828 epidemic, there were 3,396 men serving in seven regimental corps (see Table 3). In addition to performing local garrison duty, troops would also remain in Gibraltar to recover their strength for fresh campaigns in other parts of the Mediterranean or India. The majority of the military personnel resided in barracks and huts scattered throughout the entire territory. There

Corps	Number
Royal Artillery	355
Royal Engineers	102
Royal Wagon Train	5
Royal Staff Corps	20
12th Regiment	484
23rd R. Welch Fusiliers	474
42nd R. Highlanders	494
43rd Light Infantry	480
73rd Regiment	503
94th Regiment	479
Total Strength	3,396

TABLE 3. MILITARY STRENGTH AT GIBRALTAR, 1828.[32]

was little in the way of proper, separate accommodation for married soldiers, so military families were typically housed in what were formerly civilian quarters.

At the head of the military was the governor. He also held absolute power over the civilian inhabitants of Gibraltar. The power of a military governor extended into virtually every aspect of daily life and it was particularly evident in epidemic times. During the 1828 epidemic, Sir George Don held the position of Lieutenant-Governor over the Fortress and Territory of Gibraltar. A list of the colonial officials and military men that occupied positions of influence during this epidemic is presented in Table 4.

Vomito Prieto

Yellow fever is a viral disease that continues to plague humans around the globe.[35] The virus is carried from human to human (horizontal transmission) by means of the biting mosquito (the vector). In Gibraltar, the mosquito responsible for the transmission of yellow fever belongs to the genus *Aedes* and *species aegypti*. *A. aegypti* is recognized as a peridomestic mosquito species, meaning, it lives within close proximity to humans and their dwellings. Its flight range is limited, ranging between 400-1000 yards of its breeding site, though the average is generally between 25-30 yards.

This mosquito is an early-morning and afternoon feeder, and prefers human blood to other mammals. Oddly enough, the ankle area is the preferred feeding site on the human body, and feedings are only successful when temperatures are above 15 degrees Celsius. Blood feeding is characteristic of female mosquitoes since blood is needed for egg

Position	Individual
Lieutenant-Governor	Sir George Don
Military Secretary	Lt. J. Marshall
Director of Police and Town Major	Lt. Colonel Daniel Falla
Town Adjunct &Inspector of Markets[34]	Lt. Archibald Campbell
Garrison Quarter Master	J.P. Gilchrist
Barrack Master	R. Metcalfe
Judge Advocate	Thomas Jones Howell
Chaplain to the Forces	Rev. R.J. Hatchman
Provost Marshal	John Ross
Commanding Royal Engineers	Robert Pilkington
Judge - Court of Civil Pleas	William Toye
Civil Secretary	Lt. Colonel S.R. Chapman
Captain of the Port	William Sweetland
Receiver General of Revenues	H.L. Wickhouse
Inspector of Revenues	Francis Stokes
Kings Ganger	Andrew Patterson
Purveyors Clerk	R. Tucker
Medical Department	
Inspector of Hospitals and Principal Medical Officer	J. Hennen
Staff Surgeon	E. Dow
Apothecary	G. John
Hospital Assistants	G. Woods C.M. Vowell R. Laing W. Cruickshank

TABLE 4. A LIST OF MILITARY AND COLONIAL OFFICIALS CA 1828.[33]

production. Mosquitoes must first ingest viruses in blood meals from infected individuals and, after an incubation period which varies from 4 days to 2 weeks, depending on environmental temperature, then can pass the virus to other victims after biting them. The mosquito must bite the infected human in the early phase of the illness, as it is only at this stage that the virus is circulating in the blood of the victim. Because of marked seasonal fluctuations in temperature, the mosquito vector was unable to breed and bite year-round in Gibraltar, an important factor limiting epidemics in this community. Mosquito larvae die die at temperatures below 10 degrees and the adults do not survive for very long at temperatures below 5 degrees. For the adult mosquito, the

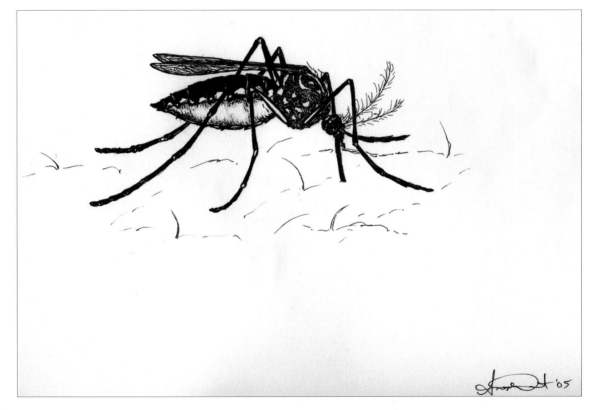

AEDES AEGYPTI (A. DAUST)

degree of activity and duration of life is largely dependent on: (1) suitable humidity, (2) shelter, and (3) access to water (to drink and breed). Breeding places are almost entirely confined to artificial collections of water. While eggs of *Aedes aegypti* are never laid on a dry surface, a wet surface appears to be preferred over water itself.[36]

The mosquito can also pass the virus via infected eggs to its offspring (called vertical transmission). Eggs are resistant to drying and can lie dormant through dry seasons, waiting to hatch until the rainy season. The mosquito egg will resist desiccation for up to one year and will hatch when flooded by water that is deoxygenated.[37] Unfortunately for Gibraltarians and other inhabitants of coastal cities, *A. aegypti* proved to be a worthy shipboard traveling companion, one infected mosquito on board a ship would be supplied with an all-you-can-eat buffet of blood meals and plenty of water storage barrels for breeding, resulting in an epidemic-in-the-making. Conditions for the spread of domestic mosquitoes were ideal in early 19th century Gibraltar, with clean still water found in tinajas, unkempt patio areas with wash barrels, and other containers.

The clinical course of yellow fever can range from mild discomfort to death. Once infected with the virus, there is an incubation period where the virus remains silent or inactive within the body from 3 to 6 days. Thereafter, two distinct phases may follow. During the 'acute phase' an individual may manifest any or some combination of the following symptoms: fever, muscle pain, headache, shivers, loss of appetite, nausea, and vomiting. After 3 to 4 days, most patients improve. About 1/8 of infected individuals will enter the potentially deadly or 'toxic phase'. The onset of this stage occurs within 24 hours.

It is at this time that the patient develops telltale signs of yellow fever: high temperature, slow pulse, a great deal of physical pain, black vomit, and yellow skin. The yellowing or jaundice is a by-product of liver damage. The black vomit, bleeding from the nose and mouth, and bloodstained stool all result from gastric bleeding and capillary damage. It is estimated that half the patients in the 'toxic phase' die within a two-week period. The remaining patients recover without any significant organ damage. Children appear better equipped than adults to withstand the virus, suffering only mild or sub-clinical symptoms. Those who survive an attack receive life-long immunity to the virus and benefit from their immunity in subsequent epidemics. The waning progress of future yellow fever epidemics in a population is related, in part, to fewer people who are susceptible (increased herd immunity), and the fact that recovered victims can no longer serve as intermediaries to pass on the virus, even though they will still be bitten by mosquitoes.

An Overview of Yellow Fever in Gibraltar

Gibraltarians were no strangers to the devastating effects of epidemic yellow fever. As Table 5 shows, while never endemic, yellow fever did appear in Gibraltar on numerous occasions.

In order for yellow fever to emerge in epidemic proportions, it was necessary for a 'delicate balance' of conditions to come together, and if these conditions were not met, Gibraltar would then have remained free of yellow fever.[38] The most important of these conditions was the introduction of the virus to the community through an infected person or mosquito. Gibraltar's strategic location and linkage to the global community via trade and colonialism greatly facilitated the

Year	Cases	Deaths		Observations
		Military	**Civilians**	
1800		217		Out of a force of 5,400 - the usual annual average of deaths at the time being about 57.
1804		864	4864	In all likelihood, the 4864 figure is probably exaggerated.
1810	23 (6 of Military)			
1813		391	508	
1814		114	132	
1828	5,534	507	1,170	
1829	6 in the Corps of Sappers.			This caused considerable anxiety in the Garrison.
1830	6 cases in the Corps of Royal Sappers and Miners			6 cases of fever have been admitted in the Ordinance Hospital from the Corps, 4 of which are severe and 3 yet doubtful.
1832	2 in the 60th Regiment			

TABLE 5. CHRONOLOGY OF YELLOW FEVER IN GIBRALTAR

possibility of the importation of this infection. Second, ecological conditions had to be suitable for the mosquito to survive, feed, and reproduce, since they are the vectors of the yellow fever virus. Such conditions were easily met in Gibraltar's hot summer months, when mosquitoes were observed to "swarm in myriads, and greatly increase the apparent heat of the atmosphere, by the state of irritation in which they constantly keep the skin"[39] A third critical factor was an ample number of susceptibles (non-immune) present in the community.[40] And by 1828, that particular condition had clearly been met through a high birth rate, and a large influx of newcomers to the Rock whohad had no prior exposure to the

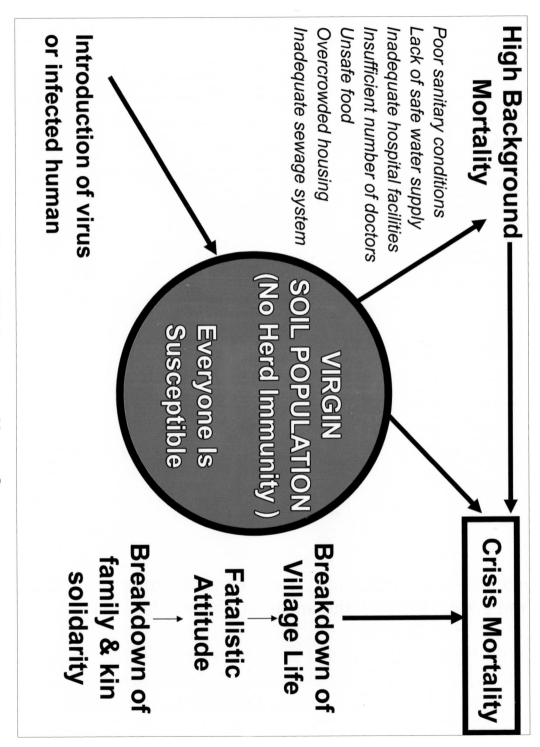

FIGURE 5. A COMMUNITY UNDER CRISIS

deadly virus.

Meeting these necessary precursors, Gibraltar further aided the development of epidemic yellow fever through its crowded and unsanitary urban landscape. Arguably, the most important factor was the local tradition of patio living, where large concentrations of potentially susceptible people resided within a limited and confined space. Further, patios offered an ideal niche for mosquito breeding, as courtyards were often poorly paved, had insufficient drainage, and were shut strong winds and direct sunlight. The daily washing and drying of clothes in these shaded and inadequately ventilated courtyards

WATER CONTAINER (TINAJA)

produced stagnant pools of water that did not dry out even during the summer droughts. Water storage containers, barrels, buckets, and earthen jugs or *tinajas*, created ideal breeding grounds for the mosquito vector. Houses lacked glass windows or screens, and mosquitoes could easily make their way through simple wooden shutters.

A TYPICAL PATIO SETTING

(K. DENNY)

Chapter One Endnotes

[1]Your fever pass, Senorita!

[2]Your pass now!

[3]Omran's theory relies on the historical mortality experience of England and Wales between the years 1790-1970.

[4]This is essential if the scholar hopes to become aware of the wide range of available evidence necessary to fathom the inherently complex history of the community. It is only with time and commitment that the investigator can earn the trust by various members of the community to gain some insight into "the insider perspective" of community life.

[5]In order to employ such a method, it is essential that the investigator embrace the fundamental determinants of population structure and dynamics by examining its ecology, biology, demography. If the approach is historical or evolutionary in perspective, the dimension of time is integral to the study.

[6]This one aspect is a salient point in the characteristic that a case study possesses. Often, the study gives a voice to the powerless and voiceless (Feagin, Orum, & Sjoberg, 1991).

[7]It is imperative that scholars question any study that is based solely on one source or one line of enquiry. It is too easy to put aside problems of personal bias and publication expediency in order to 'produce the definitive treatise of the community' after a single short field trip.

[8]Diversity in form is a central quality to the case study approach. Yin (1993) has identified two variants as (1) intrinsic (when the researcher has an interest in the case itself), and (2) instrumental (when the case is used to understand more than what is obvious to the observer).

[9]McNeil, 1976, 96.

[10]See, for example, McNeil 1976; Curtin 1989; Dobson 1989.

[11]Hennen 1830, 71.

[12]Crisis mortality can be defined as a sudden and dramatic rise in the level of mortality triggered by such agents as war, famine, and flood and epidemic disease.

[13]Yellow fever was known by many other names: for example, yellow jack, black vomit fever, the yellow scourge, Bulam fever and known in the area as Vomito prieto (dark vomit in Spanish).

[14]Such an approach is not unique to this work and examples can be found in the edited work of Herring and Swedlund, 2003.

[15]To supplement his writing and further situate the reader within time and place, a set of notes will accompany the diary. Finally, the text will follow with two additional sections; the first discussing the aftermath of the epidemic in the local setting followed by a section of notes which broaden, reflect and compare the experience of Gibraltar on a more global level.

[16]Bigelow 1831, 41.

[17]Bigelow 1831, 27.

[18]Stewart 1967, 157

[19]Sanguinetti 1993, 9.

[20]Early in the 19th century, the town proper was divided into twenty-eight districts, each with its own appointed inspector(s) to watch over health and regulate the civilian population more closely. The upper Rock consisted of districts 24, 25, 26 and 27.

[21]Robertson 1841, 165.

[22]Sanguinetti 1993, 8.

[23]Walsh 1803, 6.

[24]Rose and Rosenbaum 1991, 9.

[25]Individuals who had not survived a bout of yellow fever were forced to reside at the North Front until the epidemic had subsided. The only other civilians permitted to reside there were inhabitants of the first and second classes, who were permitted to reside in this village during the summer months. No foreigners are ever allowed to live on the North Front, except for a few ships' carpenters, blacksmiths and fishermen.

[26]CO 91/34 16 September 1787. The Commandant General of the Camp at San Roque complained to the Governor that there was construction going on beyond the limits at two sites; one of these was at Catalan Bay. This is the earliest reference to Catalan Bay and presumably sets the date of settlement no earlier than 1787.

[27]Under strict military regulations, there was little opportunity for growth in the community of Catalan Bay. Its size was limited to 300 inhabitants and only those males engaged in fishing were able to secure residence in the village. Year and population size in brackets: 1814 (211), 1834 (229), 1846 (346), 1868 (256), 1871 (261), 1878 (291), 1881 (288), 1891 (293), 1911 (288), 1921 (293) and 1931 (279).

[28]CO 91/100 Gibraltar 6 March, 1829. Abstract of the Population of Gibraltar, exclusive of the Kings Troops Town Majors Office. D. Falla. Town Major.

[29]Dwight 1824, 31.

[30]Dwight 1824, 29. Dwight's comment is rather odd given that "Rock Scorpion" was always a pejorative term, and originally applied to those of British origin born in Gibraltar. It is unlikely that native Gibraltarians would have thought of themselves as Rock Scorpions.

[31]The strength of the garrison (by year) excluding women and children are follows: 2943 (1821), 2802 (1822), 2809 (1823), 3201 (1824), 3547 (1825), 3627 (1826), 3322 (1827), 3396 (1828), 3918 (1829), 3834 (1830), 3524 (1832), 3159 (1833), 3757 (1834), and 3224 (1835). WO 334/12.

[32]WO 17/1814 August 25th 1828. Excludes wives and children of the military men stationed in Gibraltar.

[33]CO 173/6 List of individuals present in 31st of December 1827.

[34]According Hennen (1830, 82), there were also two sub-directors of police outside the garrison – military officers in charge of Catalan Bay and the villages and buildings on the Neutral Ground and North Front.

[35]Yellow fever historical milestones include: (1) the first recorded epidemic of what was thought to have been yellow fever was in the Yucatan Peninsula in 1647/8, (2) the first recorded epidemic in Africa occurred among British troops in St. Louis de Sengel in 1778; (3) Ronald Ross in 1887 proposes that mosquitoes were responsible for the transmission of yellow fever ands malaria; (5) a major breakthrough in understanding the epidemiology of yellow fever occurred in 1900 when Reed and the Yellow Fever Commission working in Cuba, documented that the disease was caused by a filterable agent (virus) transmitted by a mosquitoes, and, (6) the first effective yellow fever vaccine in discovered in 1930.

[36]Christophers, 1960.

[37]Wolmack 1993.

[38]Carrigan, 1994; Sawchuk and Burke 1998.

[39]Hennen 1830, 60.

[40]If virus-harbouring mosquitoes arise in a community but bite only those who are immune, or the mosquitoes die before biting susceptible persons, the disease will not spread. If an infected person enters a community and is not bitten by a mosquito within the first three or four days of illness, the disease will not spread.

-2-

William Thorton Gibraltar Fever Diary and Related Notes 1828

September

Monday 1

This morning the garrison was thrown into great alarm by reports having been whispered about that the yellow fever had made its appearance. The first person supposed to be affected was a servant woman living with Mr. Martin[1] who was taken ill on Saturday morning. She was removed to the house of some other person in a different direction but in the same district where she remained very bad

Tuesday 2

Today the alarm no ways abated. One of the drains has just been discovered to be completely stopped up with filth (etc) and which had not been looked to all the Season. At a small house situated very close to the above drain a man was discovered by the sagacious Dr. Woods lying on a Bed to rest himself and was by that gentleman ordered to remain at home for that he was affected with fever when it is reported that the Man declared he never was better in his life. In the evening one or two sentinels were placed at the man's house to prevent communication by so doing the greatest consternation possible prevailed

The Diarist[48]

We have only a few details of the diarist, William Thornton. He was born in Britain, and came to Gibraltar about 1807, aged 22. He is described as a shopkeeper in the 1814 census. At the time of the 1828 epidemic he was thus about 44 years old, and owned a haberdashery shop in Main Street, above which he lived.

The 1834 census describes him as a draper, aged 50, Protestant. He was married to Mary, a native-born Gibraltarian who was 36 at the time of the census. (Perhaps she was the Maria who sat up with him all night when he came down with the yellow fever). They had three sons and a daughter, all born in Gibraltar, and there were two resident servants in the home: Baptista Violetto, a 33-year-old Catholic from Genoa, and Jane Megan, a 17-year-old British Protestant.

Thornton survived the epidemic by over three decades; he died in 1869, aged 84. There is a plaque in his memory in the Anglican Cathedral. His wife Mary died in 1866. His children inherited his property, but the name has not survived in Gibraltar.

ARTIST RENDITION OF THORNTON'S SHOP

when the Authorities[2] taking the alarm it was then currently reported that the Sentinels were placed over the drain and not over the house. However this latter report is not generally believed – Mr. Martin's servant died this evening supposed to be the first case.

Wednesday 3
This morning at the suggestion of Sir G. Don four Medical Gentlemen were requested to attend to visit the different hospitals (etc) in conjunction with those medical men in the garrison and after having visited all the hospitals Spanish Church[3] and a number of houses in No 24 District[4] which is the only place at present known to be infected they one and all reported that the garrison had not been so healthy these last ten years. A fine young man Sergeant in 12 Regiment taken ill this morning

Thursday 4
Almost every person you meet this morning look pleasant and cheerful and it appears as if the whole was a dream. It is likewise now generally reported that there no longer exist anything to create serious alarm it is also reported that there is not a single new case today.[5]

Friday 5
This morning there has been more bustle than anything seen yet every person seems to be in motion with anxiety pictured in their faces. The Sergeant 12th Regiment died this morning which has considerably increased the alarm and a meeting at the Governors has completely set everything in an uproar. This afternoon the 12 Regiment

The Index Case

The diarist's first reference to a case of yellow fever is of a member of Mr. Martin's household dated the 1st of September, 1828. In all likelihood, this was not the first case, and she was most likely the eighth individual in the deadly chain of infection. The importance of determining the first (or index) case in an epidemic remains a fundamental modern day epidemiological principle. Pinpointing the index case is instructive in determining which factor(s) were responsible for the outbreak of the disease in a community. Limited by imprecise knowledge of the disease and by concealment and misreporting, it was virtually impossible to accurately reconstruct the series of events and personnel involved in the 1828 outbreak. The evidence complied by a later Board of Enquiry suggests that,

> ...the first case of the Epidemic fever occurred on the 11th or 12th of August in a Boy of the name of Fani. Thirteen years of age, who died on the 17th August with the fatal and characteristic symptoms of black-vomit and yellow skin. That the second case was his sister, aged ten years who was taken ill on the 17th and died on the 20th. That the third was their Companion and play fellow, a Boy of the name of Cafiero aged twelve years, who fell ill on the 16th or 17th and was sent to the Civil Hospital on the 21st.... It was stated that the Father was a Segar manufacturer - that he had formerly been a Seafaring Man, that his eldest son was a Boat Man. That the father frequently went into the Bay, and that on, or about the tenth of August, he went with his son and daughter, and their Companion Cafiero, on board some vessel, for the purpose, as was said, of selling Segars, where they remained for about one hour, and upon their return on shore, carried a Bag of Clothes to their home to be washed.

> The Boy as it appears was taken ill the day after, and his sister and Companion, as mentioned already.

> It was stated to the Board by a Sister of one of the crew of the Ship Dygden, and confirmed by the Girl's late Master, that she fell ill on the twentieth of August, two or three days after she had counted out some clothes, which her Brother, who had had the black-vomit fever in the Havanah, shortly before he sailed for this place, had brought on shore from that vessel to be washed.

> Three Washer-Women named Parody, Silcox and Moma, residing in district No. 24 were taken ill about the end of August, whilst employed in washing clothes belonging to Seamen of different ships. Two of these Women died. It also appears in evidence that the two first persons taken ill of the disease, out of 24 district were the Nurse Mrs Flynn, who attended the Woman Silcox in the Civil Hospital, and the maid Servant of Mr Frazer Surgeon of that establishment. That the mate of the Ship Dygden was ill about the 24th July, whilst the vessel was in

marched out to encamp on the Governors meadow and a large party of 43 Regiment actively employed from 2 in afternoon till 10 at night in erecting the Tents[6] for Civilians who are encamped near the Eastern beach. Also arrived at the Spanish lines about 200 fresh troops to reinforce all the guards there and a sort of Cordon[7] is formed to prevent Spaniards as well as English from returning into Spain, although a great number of Them came through the first thing this morning, yet those called the authorities would not allow even those of their own country to return unless they would perform twenty days quarantine and many who would willingly have performed the time stated they would not suffer to repass upon any pretence.

Several of the Engineers also are reported to day and upon the face of that report are ordered into camp close to Paco Roco Cave.[8] The bustle and confusion occasioned by removing the Troops (etc) is beyond description. The Garrison has all the appearance of a place in the vicinity of two armies preparing for Battle. The Military on one side the Burial Ground and the Civilians on the other with their respective sentinels (etc etc)

Saturday 6
There has been nothing particular today with the exception of a great many more families removing to the Neutral Ground[9] where it is said there are upwards of 200 more tents pitched for their reception. A Young Lady of the name of Francis died and was buried this morning, she was a pretty looking girl aged about 15 years.

quarantine. That one of the sailors shipped here to assist in navigating her to Cadiz, was seriously ill on board her, whilst in quarantine in that Bay. That one of the Sisters of Teste, the Health Guard of this vessel, residing in 24 district, who on the 11th August assisted to wash the clothes, which he had used on board of this vessel, was taken taken ill, according to Teste's own declaration, on the 21st August. That the clothes belonging to the two Seamen, so died on board this vessel, were sold to American Sailors, who landed here. That twenty-six vessels arrived here from yellow-fever-latitudes, between the finish of June and fourteenth of August on board of which ten Seamen had died on the passage.

Another reputable account argues against this sequence of events, and points to the Serfaty family for the index case. The following description provides this version of events,[49]

After much diligent inquiry, it appeared that no earlier authentic case of the fever could be traced than those occurred in a Jew's family of the name Serfate. One of his daughters was taken ill, either on the 9th or the 11th of August, and 2 days afterwards another; then on the 15th, the child of a man named Acres. All of these lived in different departments of the same building, and in the very worst part of the portion which I have already described "as effectively shut out from the benefit of the most refreshing winds," but, moreover in the yard into which these houses opened, there was an old wooden erection, which served the purpose of a privy, as also the opening of a drain. The said Acres stated, that both of these were very great nuisances, and that he had observed, during the 2 months he lived in the yard, very bad smells to rise from the Serfaty's apartments, stood nearest to these sources of nuisances, and the door was, in fact, not many feet from the opening of the drain. The 3 cases now alluded to were either mild or protracted, as both the Jewesses continued under the influence of the fever until September, and one of them died with all the usual fatal symptoms on the 2nd or 3rd of that month. The child of Acres had it so very slightly as never to require confinement to bed, and was relieved from all of its symptoms in a few days.

The next cases were Mr. Martin, --- whose house is situated a few hundred yards from the former. ... The first cases of the disease occurred in the families of Serfate, Acres and Martin, and all before the 20th of August. Within the next 10 days, several other houses situated in their vicinity, but particularly in the row above Mr. Martin's house, successively followed. During the next 6 days, cases multiplied so rapidly that by the 5th of September, the disease had made inroad into the majority of the houses there, which contained subjects liable to attack.

On the 30th of August, a case occurred in the Sapper's Barrack on Hargrave's Parade. This was the first which was observed beyond the precincts of the first affected portion of district ---

Sunday 7

This morning although Sunday the bustle continues equal to the two days previous, two fresh cases reported, the Church very thinly attended. Walked around the eastern side of the encampment this evening and was very much pleased to see the order and the regularity of the Camp etc. The Cordon is fixed at 50 paces. I have just been informed by Mr. W. that from a Census quietly taken of a certain description of Ladies in the Garrison previous to this alarm amounted to 2370 Souls, a plentiful scarcity of the article.

Monday 8

Today agreeable to an order issued yesterday a great many people are coming into the Garrison again but only those who have passed the Fever at some time previous.[10] There are also a great many others going out from another infected district.

Tuesday 9

This morning there appears to be more alarm than two or three days from a report spreading of a man and woman having died as it is said absolutely from want of medical aid and the people appear to be very indignant at it and nothing but complaints as to the orders issued and to the management of things generally. I understand the old woman called Mammy Dick was removed from this to the Neutral Ground in a cart with a poor old Spaniard whom she abused in a terrible manner not being content with abusing him, she beat him with a stick so much that the guard was obliged to take it from her[11]

What both accounts have in common is that the first case originated from the area known as District 24. As a result, this area attracted attention as a focus for the outbreak of the epidemic, housing a cluster of individuals who were affected by the disease.

Dr. John Hennen

John Hennen (1779-1828) was born in Ireland on 21 April, 1779, and studied medicine under his father, before going to study in Edinburgh, where he obtained his medical diploma in 1798. He was appointed in 1800 to the 40th regiment, and went with it to the Mediterranean (serving in Malta, Minorca and Gibraltar). He served through the Peninsular war in various regiments and became a staff-surgeon in 1812. He was known as a skilful operator and energetic officer, and was also noted for being never without a cigar in his mouth. After a brief spell in civilian practice in Scotland, he returned to the Army, and was put in charge of the Jesuit's Hospital in Belgium, where he treated many of the wounded from Waterloo. In 1817 he published his best-known work, "Principles of Military Surgery." At this time he was much involved with editing the Edinburgh Medical and Surgical Journal, for which he wrote a number of articles. He received the M.D. degree from Edinburgh in 1819. In 1820, he was appointed Principal Medical Officer in the Mediterranean, residing at Malta and Corfu. The study of medical topography[50] formed one of his favourite pursuits, and as one of the editors of the Edinburgh Medical and Surgical Journal between 1819 and 1821, he published a "Sketch of a Plan for Memoirs on Medical Topography".[51]

In 1826, he became Principal Medical Officer of Gibraltar, where he remained until his untimely death. At this time he completed his great work, "Sketches of the Medical Topography of the Mediterranean, which was published posthumously by his son, also Dr John Hennen. This book is an invaluable account of the way of life in Gibraltar, Malta and the Ionian Islands in the early part of the 19th Century. In this work, he discusses the previous epidemics of yellow fever in Gibraltar between 1804 and 1814, and took a balanced view about the different theories, which raised such passions among his colleagues. The list of contents in this work reflects Hennen's view of the essential elements of health and disease,

Name and geographical position; Sources of aqueous exhalation; Mountains; Climate;

Wednesday 10

Persons generally speaking look with long anxious faces, at the Civilian Encampment. There has been four deaths today and six removed the Hospital or Lazarot. The whole of the Civilian Doctors are to put on the Staff and to receive 7/6 Per Diem and each appointed to a respective district. The English in the garrison and the Spanish outside. To day a young man lately living with Mr. Weir was removed to the Hospital absolutely taken ill from fright. Dr. S. tells me he is a bad subject.

Thursday 11

Nothing particular to day except that the disease seems rather to be increasing than anything else. This evening John Powell a young man who has been living in our house for about 2 years began to complain of a headache and went to bed early. Died 4

Friday 12

The Garrison begins to look very melancholy. All the conversation in the place now is whether or not the Fever has actually been brought into those districts or whether it has been lying dormant for sometime, but I believe the general opinion is that it was brought into the Place. Mr. Powell confined to his bed. Died 5

Saturday 13

The alarm and disease is still increasing and unfortunately it has made considerable progress among some of the Troops which are accordingly ordered into Camp. Things look very dreary, business dreadfully bad. What will be

Rains; Soil; Unhealthy situations; Vegetable, animal and mineral products; Agriculture and horticulture; Roads and communications; Population; Dwellings; Furniture, bedding, clothing; Diet; Employments, amusements, &c; Police; The civil hospital; Endemic and epidemic diseases; Marriage, births, deaths; Epizooties and diseases of plants; Popular medicine and state of physic and surgery; Longevity; Works connected with the topography, natural history, diseases &c, of Gibraltar; Medical instruction, museum libraries; Barracks; Mode of living of the troops; Hospitals

When yellow fever struck again in Gibraltar in 1828, John Hennen immediately put into effect all precautions which in those days were thought to protect the population against the disease. He enjoyed the full confidence of the Lieutenant Governor, General Sir George Don, who had no hesitation in carrying out Hennen's suggestions.

District 24

District 24 was located in the upper portions of the town, and like most of the housing in this portion of the Rock, the area was unsanitary, cramped, and grossly deficient in the basic amenities. District 24 represented a focus for the outbreak of the epidemic, housing a cluster of individuals who were affected by the disease. Furthermore, it was also claimed that tenements in this area were "most unfavourably hemmed in from free ventilation and thus as regards, it forms a focus both for the direct and reflected rays of the Sun". Authorities were quick to seize upon the fact that deplorable living conditions in this district contributed directly to the outbreak of the disease,

> The general filthy state of the District I might also remark on, but it is enough to say, that it was so bad, at the commencement of the Epidemic as to call from Dr. Hennen, then principal Medical Officer of the Garrison in a Report on the subject to the Lieutenant Governor, the unequivocal observation, that on personal examination, he had found it in such a state as not only to explain how the fever had appeared there – but to excite his Wonder that it had not done so much sooner.[53]

end of all this God Almighty only knows. Mr. Powell is unfortunately worse to day. Dr. Foote has ordered very strong medicine etc. Died 5

Sunday 14
All places of worship being closed according to Governors Order. I have therefore been into the Bay to Fish, remained there about an hour and got very sick, came on shore. Turned into Bed for an hour, got up wash etc. went down and ate an astonishing dinner and drank plenty of wine, never felt better in my life. In the evening walked around Europa where I found 23 Regiment in Camp. When I returned was just in time to see poor Powell breathe his last which was at 7 O'clock precisely.

Monday 15
This morning at ½ past 5 and accompanied by Mr. Francis attended the remains of poor Powell to its last home; he was only 23 years of age but from an infant had been very delicate. He died almost without a struggle.

This Evening at 7 O'clock Mrs. White breathed her last at Major Boyles on the Neutral Ground. This unfortunate Lady had taken her Children to Campo[12] to avoid the Fever that was raging, when she unfortunately was thrown from her Rig and received a wound. I believe in the thigh which not having received the treatment proper from the Spanish Doctors a mortification took place which terminated as above.

This morning that unfortunate young man Mr Nelson

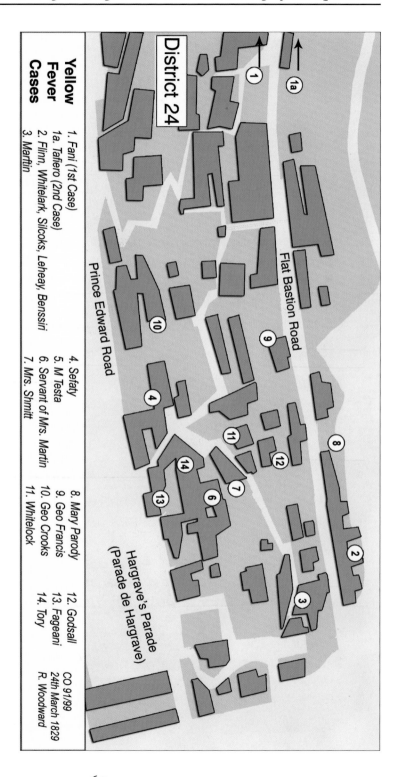

District 24

Flat Bastion Road

Prince Edward Road

Hargrave's Parade
(Parade de Hargrave)

Yellow Fever Cases			
1. Fani (1st Case)	4. Sefaty	8. Mary Parody	12. Godsall
1a. Tafiero (2nd Case)	5. M Testa	9. Geo Francis	13. Fageani
2. Flinn, Whitelark, Silcoks, Leheay, Benssiri	6. Servant of Mrs. Martin	10. Geo Crooks	14. Tory
3. Martlin	7. Mrs. Shmitt	11. Whitelock	
			CO 91/99
			24th March 1829
			R. Woodward

A MAP OF DISTRICT 24 (CHERVIN, 1830. MODIFIED BY K. JONES)

died and was buried sadly, a fine young fellow - aged about 27 years died from nothing but fear.

[13]Tuesday 16

From this wind the Rock is completely covered with Clouds which of course makes it very damp and unpleasant. There are a great number of fresh cases this morning and have continued to increase during the day

This morning also came into the Bay the Brig Oscar. Cap. Hinderwell in 16 days from Arcila and obliged to Anchor for having one of his pumps broken it was necessary to have it put in order. The captain dined with us to day and at night Rev. Mendez and myself went on board to sleep. Died 3

Wednesday 17

The most disagreeable day possible have not had one so bad for some months, in consequence the disease has considerably increased the number at the different hospitals. The deaths also have been more numerous, although the virulence of the disease has considerably abated as the principal part of the cases now admitted are slight in comparison.

That fine Gentlemanly Young Officer Lieut. Bull R. E.[14] died this Evening. Universally lamented and respected by his brother Officers and friends.

Thursday 18

The symptoms today from report are more favourable

not more than two or three admitted to Hospital and not more than 1 or two deaths. Mr. W. am sorry to say is not well this morning. from eating some Cold Fish last night. Dr Foote has administered very strong medicine which happily has had the desired effect of relieving him from a great deal of pain. Lieut. Bull was buried this morning at the Sand Pitts[15] attended only by a few of his brother Officers Died 5

[16]**Friday 19**
A report handed me by Dr Thurston[17] this morning where it is stated that the number of Cases were 429 and deaths 71. Now this report is only the actual cases of the prevailing Fever. The authorities are removing a great number of other persons out of the Garrison as well as many of those who returned a short time since belonging to the District 24 Died 4

Saturday 20
This morning Brig Oscar sailed for England, Rev. Patten and another gentleman passengers.

Am happy to say Rev. W. is much better This Morning, although not quite the thing business continues miserable, but am very sorry to say the disease is gaining ground very fast notwithstanding, there are many thousands removed from the Garrison, there have been several of the 42 Regiment released from Guard in consequence of being taken ill Died 8

GIBRALTARIANS ENCAMPED IN THE NEUTRAL GROUND (J. RUBY)

Sunday 21
This morning strong East Wind which no doubt will add a great many more to the daily reports. The deaths reported are 11 but the increase of severe cases has exceeded anything yet in This Fever. I took a ride round Europa Point this evening found it delightful and pleasant a number of Carriages out also the band of 23 Regiment Died 8

Monday 22
Dr Hennan is issuing proclamations in all directions this morning respecting personal cleanliness and about the medicine proper for persons to take when they find themselves attacked by the Fever also the symptoms attending such attack. The 42 Regiment are gone into Camp this Evening we have now not a Regiment remaining inside the garrison. Mr Lliwellyn died and was buried this morning, this man was a very timid subject in any sickness however trifling. The deaths in all are 98 and cases 571 up to day. Died 11

Tuesday 23
The Doctors reports to this morning are very heavy and the fever is now allowed by all to be increasing considerably beyond what was first expected. The Deaths are (11) more than any morning yet the weather very hot and unpleasant. Am sorry to say it has broken out among the Artillery, they have already lost several men as well as women and children. An Old Priest belonging to Spanish Church Died this morning and he has left a great deal of money to a few individuals. Died 11

Gibraltar's Board of Health

This first Board of Health consisted of three Army Medical Officers – Bolton, Fellowes and Pym – and four respectable merchants (all of Protestant British stock, of course) – Messrs. Smith, Moss, Allardyce and Rankine.

In January 1805, just after the cessation of the great epidemic, they produced a report for the Lieutenant-Governor, outlining their recommendations for the prevention of future epidemics. Given the presence – indeed, the dominance – of Pym, it was inevitable that the greatest stress was put on the prevention of importation and contagion.

They proposed building a lazaretto in Catalan Bay (or "Catalonia Bay" as the report has it – and two ships in the Bay to be used as floating lazarettos. No ships with unclean Bills of Health should be allowed to anchor, and even those with clean Bills of Health were to be boarded by a medical practitioner who would satisfy himself of the health of all members of the crew. Two Health Guards were to be posted at the landing places to prevent unauthorised communication with the shore, and two guard boats were to patrol 24 hours a day in the vicinity of the Old and New Moles.

Commerce, however, seemed to overrule health considerations: Smugglers were to be allowed in, and could stay for a few days, if they had money or goods "for the purpose of purchasing British manufacture, tobacco or Colonial produce!" Even they were subject to health checks, and were the responsibility of the persons with which they lodged.

The town was to be divided into districts, each under the supervision of respectable civil inhabitants, who would inspect houses in their district and report lack of hygiene and overcrowding. All these inspectors and health guards could call on the military to enforce their authority.

The possible ill effects of "miasmas" was not totally neglected. It was proposed that the Government should construct a main sewer, and householders would be obliged to build communicating drains from their houses. "Centrical" spots were to be established in the town where garbage was to be placed, to be carried off daily by carts. Dwellings where the fever had struck were to be cleansed with lime

Wednesday 24
The Garrison is almost deserted. There are less people to be seen today than I could have supposed it possible particularly in this Street (Waterport) which a short time since wore the appearance of Cheapside and A... Those few persons who are to be seen look many of them in great fright and not knowing what to do. The deaths today are 10

Thursday 25
This day there has been nothing particular, although the wind has been blowing fresh from the Eastward which of course has made it damp and unpleasant and a day by no means calculated to decrease the fever. The deaths today are 14

Friday 26
This morning we were visited by a shower of rain which according to the general opinion will be very prejudicial to health. It lasted only a short time when the Sun shone out bright and very hot; the increase of patients to the Hospital amounted to 100. One of them being Miss Cresswell. Died 12

Saturday 27
This morning the Sun very hot and everything unfortunately seems to be in favor of the fever. A great many more people removing from the Garrison to Neutral Ground and on board Ship, also a number of Moors left for Barbary. The disease is still increasing and what it would have been had not Dr Hennan applied such prompt and active measures God only knows. This day came in the Bucepfields

and hot water, and the walls scrubbed and painted. Curing of hides was not to be permitted within the town walls.

Medical practitioners, Roman Catholic priests, and the heads of the Hebrew community were to be ordered by proclamation to inform the authorities about all cases of sickness. No one was to practise as a doctor or apothecary without a certificate from the Inspector of Health, and approved by the Lieutenant-Governor. Many of these ideas were good, and some were put into practice. A proper sewage system and efficient street scavenging had to wait for a further decade and two more epidemics, with the arrival of the energetic General Don.

General Sir George Don (1754-1832) had been Lieutenant Governor of Gibraltar since 1814. He arrived during the yellow fever epidemic of that year and immediately set about improving sanitary conditions in Gibraltar. He also opened a hospital for civilians, and improved the hospital facilities for the military. As a result, Gibraltar remained free of serious epidemics for fourteen years, at a time when devastating yellow fever epidemics had raged in Spain, and bubonic plague threatened Europe from Morocco.

He was undoubtedly motivated by his concern for the health of the troops,which he commanded. He had experienced the damage that could be caused by disease in an enclosed garrison, firstly as a young officer during the siege of Fort St. Philip in Minorca in 1782. And later, when he was put

PORTRAIT OF SIR GEORGE DON (GM)

in command of the evacuation from the island of Walcheren in 1809, the invading forces had been reduced to a pitiful remnant by the "Walcheren ague" due to disease. It was natural, therefore, that he should place such an

from London   Died 13

Sunday 28
This has been an unfortunate day from the number of Deaths amongst them. Am sorry to name Miss Elizabeth Creswell[18], a very nice girl and also Mr. Duplises, managing young Man at Mons Bonetis. And what makes this case more distressing is he supposed he had passed this fever in New York some years since and his wife a very nice woman with two pretty children were at St Roque to avoid this sickness when he unfortunately breathed his last. Died 16

Monday 29
This day from the reports in circulation the disease is a little checked but how far these reports are correct I have my doubts as in the military departments I am convinced it is still increasing. Things look very gloomy indeed. This morning received 100 super India Handkerchiefs[19] and cannot sell a single piece, which at another time would have sold instantly. Found myself very queer began to think I had caught it but thank God soon got better.   Died 17

Tuesday 30
Every person you see or speak to, their conversation is upon the daily increase of this dreadful sickness. this morning a young Lady named Hardy died aged about 13 years a very pretty genteel girl - Went for a ride this evening round Europa where it was very cool and pleasant that very pleasant gentlemanly old man Mr Cresswell removed to the

PROCLAMATION.

BY HIS EXCELLENCY SIR GEORGE DON, KNIGHT GRAND CROSS OF THE MOST HONOURABLE MILITARY ORDER OF THE BATH, KNIGHT GRAND CROSS OF THE ROYAL GUELPHIC ORDER, AND OF THE ROYAL ORDER OF MILITARY MERIT OF FRANCE, GENERAL OF HIS MAJESTY's FORCES, AND COLONEL OF THE THIRTY-SIXTH REGIMENT OF FOOT, LIEUT.-GOVERNOR AND COMMANDER-IN-CHIEF OF THE GARRISON AND TERRITORY OF GIBRALTAR &c. &c. &c.

Whereas a disease, highly dangerous to the public health, exists in this Fortress, and as it is expedient that every endeavour should be used to prevent its clandestine introduction into the neighbouring Countries;

It is ordered that no Vessel, or Craft, under Forty Tons burthen, be permitted to clear out at, or to depart from, this Port, without a special Permission for that purpose from His Excellency the LIEUT.-GOVERNOR, on the application of the Captain of the Port.

GEORGE DON,
General and Lieut.-Governor.

Head-Quarters, Gibraltar,
October 6, 1828.

By Command,

S. R. CHAPMAN, Civil Secretary.

A PROCLAMATION ISSUED DURING THE EPIDEMIC (GA)

the neutral ground to avoid if possible the sickness which unfortunately prevails in his own Farm on the Rock. Mrs Cresswell and the other daughter am sorry to say are very ill   Died 18

October

Wednesday 1
This morning almost the first thing was told of the Death of Miss Bella Slaturga, Mrs D Lopez, a very fine tall woman perhaps as any in the Garrison.

A short time afterwards of Mr Frost, this man to all appearance was getting quite well he got up in the morning washed and dressed himself and requested to have some milk and bread for his breakfast when he was suddenly seized with a shivering and almost instantly expired. In the Evening a person called from the Ordnance hospital to say that Richard Turner was also dead it appears from the statement of the man who attended him that he struggled very hard with his mortal foe. Died 18

Thursday 2
About 2 o'clock a smart shower of rain fell but soon passed off having the whole garrison disappointed. To day Mr. W with two or three other Gentlemen attended the remains of the late R. Turner to their last home, and William Oxberry[20] (in going to take the horse to Mr Wearing who was waiting at William Adams) in passing a Mule loaded with straw and at his usual quick rate of riding in the Street came in contact with the straw. By some means or other

emphasis on prevention of epidemics, and sad that when an epidemic finally came, he was past his prime, and exposed to criticism by his detractors. This criticism was surely unjustified; his policy had always been to take the best medical advice, and if there were conflicting medical opinions, to take action as if both theories were correct. He wrote concerning the yellow fever in 1814, when he had just arrived in Gibraltar:"…having received from Medical persons…the most apposite and plausible opinions, some tending to prove it endemic, others epidemic, contagious and infectious, I have determined to consider it all four."[54]

Deadly Vapours

On September 5th 1828, the young, pretty, fifteen year old daughter of George Francis succumbed to the ravages of yellow fever. At the time of the epidemic, ithe Francis family consisted of fifteen individuals and lived in District 24.[55] Both Mr. and Mrs. Francis had passed through the fever in an earlier epidemic. The day before their daughter's death, Mr. Francis had separated the sick from the healthy children. At the same time, he sent three of his children to the South. One of these children returned home sick on the very same day of their departure.

The fifteen year old daughter became affected on the afternoon of the 2nd September, but did not attract attention until the morning of the 3rd. Until she saw the black vomit, Mrs. Francis insisted that her daughter's illness was the result of her having eaten too much of a fruit pie the previous Sunday. She died on the 5th. The Francis family's physician, Peter Wilson, describes his meeting with the family,[56]

> On the morning after her Death, I had paid the Family a visit, and was on my way from the House, when the father, overtaking me in the Street, said he had a very curious circumstance to relate, which had only last night come to his Wife's recollection; namely the Girl having told her on returning home on the afternoon of the 2nd that she had stood for some time at the boundary Wall which overlooks Mr. Martin's Premises, and spoke to W. Martin's Children, who were in the yard below, and that she concluded this remark with the expression, "O Mother what a bad smell comes up from that Drain. I felt something warm go up my bosom, which has made me quite sick."

This passage clearly illustrates the common belief that 'bad smells' or miasma vapours could be the source of infection and illness, and were particularly feared when epidemics appeared.

when he was dragged off the saddle and in falling broke the bone of his left arm. He was taken to Dr Mathias[21] who happened fortunately to be at home he immediately set the bone and he is now going on well. Died 14

Friday 3
This morning Mr W visited Mr Creswell at his new habitation and am very sorry to say found him ill and very low spirited. Yet could not resist from telling a few anecdotes in his usual good humoured way. Sir W likewise visited Mr Lowe, Mr Thompson, Will Heathcote etc etc and found them all well. but Mr Thompson as much frightened as ever and will not let any person from the Garrison come near him by some yards if he can possibly avoid it. Died 20

Saturday 4
Nothing of particular importance today with the exception of several sentries being relieved from guard at Ragged Staff which place appears from the statement of the soldiers to be very much infected Died 24

Sunday 5
To day am very sorry to hear of the immense increase of cases and the Deaths are rather more than any day previous yet the deaths in the Medical return do not come up to the number that has passed the Barrier Gates at the place the number is between 30 and 40.

Among the deaths am very sorry to add that of the beautiful Miss Mary Creswell (who with her sister last Sunday)

VAPOURS RISING FROM STREET SEWERS

have fallen victims to this disease. Among the deaths am very sorry to add that of the beautiful Miss Mary Creswell (who with her sister last Sunday) have fallen victims to this disease. Died 27

Monday 6
This day there appears to be nothing particular with the exception of a number of Military Officers reported sick and one gentleman belonging to Ordnance department dead. The middle of this day intensely hot so much so that was almost afraid to breathe.[22] Died 24

Tuesday 7
The reports of the disease among the military are distressing beyond any thing this morning not a Corps in the Garrison but are suffering more or less. Even the 73 Regiment which have been stationed at Windmill Hill[23] ever since they have been here are now ordered into Camp having previously lost a number of men the number of Military Officers reported today are 17. Died 24

Wednesday 8
This morning it was reported that the Fever has made its appearance at The Governor's Cottage but in the course of the day a dispatch came to the Convent to contradict the report circulated. The disease continues to rage with great violence amongst all the military in the Garrison. The artillery are all of them ordered into amp in different parts. Died 29

Neutral Ground

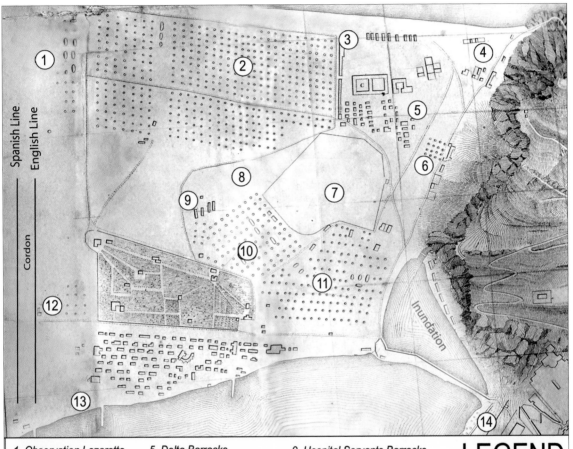

Spanish Line
English Line
Cordon

1. Observation Lazaretto
2. Civil Camp
3. East Barracks
4. Devils Tower
5. Delta Barracks
6. Miner & Sappers Camp
7. Cemetery
8. Jewish Cemetery
9. Hospital Servants Barracks
10. Hegiment Women's Camp
11. Military Camp
12. Guard Station
13. West Barracks
14. Lazaretto

LEGEND

**A MAP OF THE NEUTRAL GROUND DURING THE EPIDEMIC
(CHERVIN, 1830, MODIFIED BY K. JONES)**

Thursday 9
This morning very fine and continued through the day at night it came into blow a perfect hurricane so much so that a great quantity of Tents on the Neutral Ground were completely blown away and the poor inhabitants of them put to much inconvenience.

An Order came to the Cordon to admit no more letters but through the regular Bag and on the proper post days. This is consequence of some stupid individual infringing the health regulation established by attempting to pass a silk Handkerchief in a letter.[24] Died 22

Friday 10
This morning suppose from William Oxberry dancing about all over the house he has taken a severe cold which has brought on the fever he has been removed to his father's house where he is going on tolerably well. In addition to going about without his jacket has been eating a great many grapes. - but his father appears very high and says his son caught the fever in consequence of Antonios coming back to the house so soon after he had got better. Died 23

Saturday 11
This morning the Man servant Jose was taken ill and Mr Wearing took him immediately to Hospital. From the immense increase of the patients at the latter place they have been obliged to convert the New Church into use of those unfortunates they cannot receive. The Rev Mr Hatchman[25] is very bad today in fact Dr Wilson[26] seems to think there is hardly a chance for him   Died 16

The Handkerchief Incident

The diarist and the Governor make reference to the handkerchief incident of October 9th, when an individual in Gibraltar attempted to introduce a silk handkerchief into Spain through the mail. Since the handkerchief was viewed as a potential source of infection, this event caused great distress and consternation among health authorities on both sides of the border in Spain and Gibraltar. In fact, following the advice of Gibraltar's Board of Health, a Quarantine Proclamation was issued in 1830 which cited any article made of silk as particularly liable to retain infection. A partial listing of the goods, wares, and merchandise that were viewed as potentially suspect in the time of an epidemic or sickness is reproduced below:[57]

Apparel of all kinds,
Artificial flowers
Beads, Bracelets or Necklaces in strings
Beds, Mattresses, Mats
Books, Maps, Paper, Parchment
Brushes of all sorts
Canvass
Carpets
Cordage, not tarred
Cotton, Linen, Wool, Yarn, Thread
Down, Feathers
Flax
Gold or Silver on Thread, Cotton, Hair Wool or Silk
Hats, Caps or Bonnets
Hemp
Hoofs
Hair of all sorts
Nets
Quills
Rags
Sails and Sail Cloth
Silk
Skins, Hides, Fur, Leather
Sponges
Vellum
Wool

Dr Foote handed me the following statement of cases up to this day

Cases 2500 deaths 500

Remaining sick 771

Serious 344 slight 217 convalescent 210

Officers dead 5 doctors do 3

Sunday 12

The reports to day seem as if they would be very heavy. The number of new cases have reported to be 146 and for the most part serious ones. Our Maria has been complaining these last few days. She says from a severe cold. She must have taken in leaving off a gown that was lined and going in short sleeves. I am a little inclined to think it is the fever. W Oxberry is rather better to day although the doctor expects the fever to return at night. Died 31[27]

Monday 13

Today the Town Sergeants etc are very busy turning out a number of other families from different parts of the Garrison. This morning am very sorry to say The Rev Hatchman[28] died. He was buried at the South. Likewise a very fine tall man whose name was Gonzales. He was a Spanish broker and a friend of Mr Mendez and a man you would have thought would almost live forever from his appearance but so treacherous is this disease that a man is gone in an instant   Died 25

Tuesday 14

This morning a very great demand for that very unpleasant sounding machine, The Dead Cart, move in whatever

Gibraltar's Quarantine Regulations

In order to protect the health and well-being of its citizens, state authorities often resorted to the adoption of quarantine. Quarantine regulations in Gibraltar date back to at least the mid-18th century, when, despite fear of the plague, communication with Africa was an economic necessity that prompted authorities to institute a series of precautionary measures.[58] According to one 19th century physician,

> [in] Gibraltar, where there are no purifying lazarettos, and where the limited extent of territory, and other peculiarities, preclude the possibility of such establishments, precautionary measures, until very recently, have chiefly consisted in protracted quarantine, immersion in water, and careful ablution of every thing belonging to the crew, and passengers of ships arriving from suspected places, before they were admitted to what is termed pratique, or free intercourse with the community.[59]

The fundamental principle underlying quarantine regulations was the belief that diseases could be imported with the arrival of people, animals, ships, and goods from places experiencing an epidemic.[60] While Gibraltar's quarantine regulations were less liberal than those of many Mediterranean countries (for example, France, Portugal, Italy, Tunis), a lack of harmony with Spanish quarantine regulations presented numerous problems for Gibraltarians throughout the 19th century. Quarantine practices in these two neighbouring countries differed materially. In Spain, there were two forms of quarantine: one of observation, and one of strict quarantine. In the former, it was not necessary that cargo be discharged. In the latter, fumigation was to take place before certain specified goods could land. In Gibraltar, vessels could only undergo a quarantine of observation and infected vessels with access to a lazaretto could not be dealt with at all.

Since quarantines could threaten the economic vitality of port communities, it is not surprising that those engaged in and reliant on 'business as usual' were the most opposed to the view that diseases could be imported into communities via people, animals, food, and other materials brought to port by ships. Generally, every effort would be made to argue that it was entirely unnecessary to close or otherwise disable a port's activities. When the 19th century French colony of Saint-Louis-du-Sénégal became plagued by recurring yellow fever outbreaks, Ngalamulume found that "French, British and Portuguese merchants who were angry about...

direction you will you are annoyed either with the sight or sound of them.[29] This evening at seven O'clock William Oxberry breathed his last, I am still of opinion that this Boys fever was brought on from Cold and eating a quantity of fruit and from not taking the advice of different persons as to taking cold. Died 30

Wednesday 15
This morning the Duke of York Steam Boat came into the Bay from London in 15 days the only person for this place are Dr Mr Broadfoot who have been put on board the Cutter. - she proceeded again immediately up to Genoa for which place it appears she had a number of Greek Ambassadors, and all the Goods and Medicines etc taken with her which is a great inconvenience as respects the medicine that at this time not of so much consequence. W. Oxberry was buried this morning at 8 O'clock Mr Wearing and George attended - a most beautiful morning as it is possible to be. Died 26

Thursday 16
This day commences with a very strong wind from the Eastward and continues very black and cloudy throughout. This morning Mr Cochrane at Lapoulides is taken ill as well as Mr David Ingles. The number of patients remaining in the different Hospitals this evening amounts to 1015 and 21 Military Officers amongst the latter am happy to state that Mr Harris Adjutant 43 Regt is getting much better. Died 30

[interruptions in trade]...wanted to avoid medical inspections and quarantines at all costs".[61] To do so, they adopted a very convenient cover-up for yellow fever, arguing that sick individuals arriving in port aboard ships were suffering from "ordinary African fever," a disease argued to be confined to native Africans. In so doing, "it was presented as a fever that was natural to Africans and did not require any special medical attention, thus corroborating the idea that as long as a disease affected the natives, it did not require intervention" and economic activities could proceed uninterrupted.[62] In Gibraltar, the desire to maintain an open and unfettered marketplace was not only at risk because of outbreaks of yellow fever since many other infectious disease epidemics caused similar threats. During the 1865 cholera epidemic, for ex-

PROVISIONS COMING IN FROM SPAIN

Friday 17
This morning the atmosphere very heavy and dense apparently inclining to rain which of course would be very acceptable. Amongst the great number of deaths today am sorry to name a Miss Bane niece of Mr Farquhars amongst the number a native I believe of Scotland. have not heard of any other persons today that we particularly know. The appearance of a change of wind   Died 33

Saturday 18
To day the weather is much the same as yesterday it being considerably hotter this last day or two than it has been for some time past the number of admissions to the Hospitals has of course increased and the dead carts (now 3 in number) have been kept constantly employed the whole day. This evening came back the Zephyr Schooner having been dismasted off Cadez. She sailed from this one week to day since.   Died 29

Sunday 19
This morning Mr Mendez knocked at my door before I was properly awake to know if I had heard of the death of Mr Cochrane at Lapoulides. He died at three O'clock universally respected and was buried at about noon. Attended by several very respectable Gentlemen amongst the latter were Mr Turner Lapoulides etc etc. I went to bathe this day at Noon and found the water delightful and pleasant. Died 32

Monday 20
There has been nothing of any consequence today but the

ample, merchants in Gibraltar opposed publication of details of the progress of the epidemic in the Gibraltar Chronicle for fear that it would harm trade.[63]

The Sanitary Cordon and Special Marketplace

Quarantine control was equally complex on land routes. Sanitary cordons, land barriers where only those with a clean bill of health could pass, were established to prevent the entry of a contagious agent. Such cordons were generally temporary measures assembled for the duration of a perceived threat. They consisted of medical inspector(s), bureaucrats, and military presence for enforcement. As the sanitary cordons often stretched for miles, their administration required organization, co-operation, and freedom from corruption to

THE PALLENQUE
(MODIFIED FROM 'THE GRAPHIC', JULY 26 1884, J. PADIAK)

disease still goes on increasing a sweep a great number of persons off daily in fact Dr. Hennan himself is of opinion that we may add 25 Percent daily to the returns that are made. Died 23

Tuesday 21
From a notice in the Chronicle[30] of this day there are no boats from the Garrison to proceed farther North than the Watering Place just beyond the Neutral Ground upon pain of being fined upon by the Spanish Sentinels. - As a few days since two or three boats approached close in shore. Some fisherman drawing their nets on shore this on the eastern beach drew also the body of a pretty Spanish woman on shore who it is supposed threw herself from off some of those high rocks leading to Catalan Bay. She was recognized as a woman very much attached to the late Mr Cochrane. The rain commences at 4 O 'clock Died 15

Wednesday 22
The weather has had the appearance of much rain falling but unfortunately the clouds dispersed almost as soon as gathered in Spain and Barbary. There has been a great deal of rain accompanied by much Lightning and Thunder. The Spanish Almanack prophesized a very heavy storm at - Gibraltar late this night or early on the following but I am very sorry to say there is no appearance of any at present. Died 12

Thursday 23
I am in hopes with Gods blessing that this dreadful disease is now on the decrease from the weather being colder than for some

operate well.[64] There were generally two kinds of stations: those for the passage of goods only (such as letters, money, and small goods), and larger stations for the movement of imports and people. To make the cordon effective, contaminated and uncontaminated persons were kept separate and merchandise was handled with iron tongs. Money was immersed in vinegar for disinfection.

Gibraltar and Spain had established an unusual means of economic accommodation or marketplace during period of epidemic: the pallenque. The idea of the pallenque appears to date back to autumn of 1810 when yellow fever appeared in Spain. Fearful of the spread of yellow fever into the garrison, Lieutenant-Governor Campbell ordered that,

> [all] communication with Spain by land [cease] excepting what be necessary to provide Provisions, for which purpose a market has been established outside the Bayside barrier where all articles of provisions are received whether animal or vegetable with certain Precautions.[65]

Under this scheme, provisions were passed through a designated space at the Lines, set off by two lines of posts and ropes about 200 feet apart. This special marketplace permitted, in theory at least, a highly regulated means of communication between the two trading partners. The exchange of goods was straightforward. To begin, the Spaniards would place provisions in the middle of this area and then retire to their side. The merchant dealers of Gibraltar enter into bartering an agreeable price. Money would be left in small packages to be picked up by Spanish police with tongs and dipped in vinegar before handing to the seller. Vegetables, fruit, fowl, straw, and charcoal were all exchanged in this manner. From the British side, Gibraltar's Director of Police[66] would oversee the transactions, keeping a watchful idea for any improprieties. Direct communication across the border was accomplished by yelling or through the exchange of letters. However, similar to the practice in other countries, all mail was first dipped in vinegar before passing through the sanitary cordon. After passing through the cordon, envelopes were pierced and then fumigated.

time past. There has been nothing particular today Died 18

Friday 24
This day something like yesterday, the air quite cool morning and evening. The admissions to day am happy to say are considerably decreased and most people are of opinion that please God this weather continues or that we have rain we shall in the course of a short time be rid of dreadful sickness. Died 21

Saturday 25
To day another change in the weather but for the worse instead of the cool breeze we have enjoyed for the last day or two we have now that disagreeable close heavy atmosphere so injurious to health even at the most healthy season. The number of patients a little increased   Died 10

Sunday 26
This is a very fine and beautiful morning with the sun shining on the Rock most delightfully. Am very sorry to hear of the decease of that very much gentlemanly man Dr. Matthias who was taken ill only Thursday night. He has I believe left a wife and large family to bewail his loss. Likewise was told of the death of that young man named Barbar, Methodist Preacher, who it appears has been acting as Chaplain since the death of Rev Hatchman. This young man is supposed to have taken the Fever whilst attending a patient in the Hospital who wished to confess something and being very much exhausted Mr B was obliged to lean quite over him to hear what he had to say and from that circumstance supposed he took it. Died 21

Treatment of Yellow Fever

At the time of the deadly visitations of yellow fever to Gibraltar, physicians could offer little in the way of medical treatment for infectious disease except rest, food and compassion. Unable to explain the cause and course of the epidemic, local doctors were limited in their ability to treat their patients successfully. In fact, there was considerable divergence of opinion as to the best method of treatment: bleeding and topical bleeding with leeches, purgation to keep bowels open, cold affusion with vinegar and water to cool the skin, tepid affusion or fomentations to relieve pain, or diminution of urine, to allay vomiting the use of soda water, Spruce beer and Port, and the application of large doses of purgatives and calomel. Warm baths were considered useful in later stages for pain and prostration. In severe cases, doctors used mercury for its purgative qualities. Calomel, a chalky mercury compound, was the standby of many doctors and was administered in doses large enough to produce bleeding gums, a sign of mercury poisoning. For example, Dr. Gilpin during the 1813/14 yellow fever epidemics wrote: "in the general mode of treatment, the medical officers of the garrison, are I believe agreed. Calomel, given at first, in rather a full dose, and afterwards in smaller ones at the distance of three or four hours, seems to be the means pursued," and to calm the extreme irritability of the stomach, "the application of a blister – a tablespoon given at short intervals of an equal mixture of lime water and milk – solid opium in doses of half a grain or more very two or three hours – pills made of cayenne pepper – brandy &c."[68]

The value of calomel and mercury ointment in the treatment of yellow fever was not universally agreed as is illustrated in the Barry court martial proceedings. Elsewhere in the world, and some years earlier, a prominent medical doctor in Philadelphia, Dr. Benjamin Rush, developed quite a reputation for the treatment he developed during the city's 1793 yellow fever outbreak. A physician who ascribed to the practice of 'heroic medicine', Rush did not sit idly by his patients, instead adopting an aggressive treatment based on 'depletion' through the use of "powerful purgatives", particularly calomel, and "copious bloodletting".[69] Rush's approach ran contrary to popular opinion and provoked some opposition among his medical colleagues, since, according to Kopperman,

> Almost all writers warned against the use of emetics in treating yellow fever, their objection being that vomiting weakened patients who were already debilitated, and that

Monday 27
This morning very early was awoke by its raining tremendously hard three or four times for about a minute each time and then almost ceased. And as this day advanced it totally ceased and this day upon the whole cleared up very fine independent of the rain there has been nothing particular to day. – a brig of War came in from England this morning bringing with her four Doctors for the Garrison.[31] Died 14

Tuesday 28
There has been nothing of the least consequence to day. Although the day has been very fine. A beautiful Sloop of War and a Bomb-Ketch went into Algeciras from Tangier.[32] Died 19

Wednesday 29
I have just learnt from Mr Brown that Dr Hennan is taken ill this morning. - Miss H are now almost recovered this evening died. Miss W's pretty little bird the
red cap or Indian sparrow. the poor little creature has been ill ever since Mr Powell died. Died 25

Thursday 30
This morning the Clouds very black and Heavy with every appearance of plentiful showers but in the course of half an hour the whole dispersed and gone. the Sloop of War and Bomb-Ketch saluted Algeciras and the Island this morning. Died 15

since nausea regularly attended yellow fever, emetics might well provoke vomiting that was uncontrollable and ultimately fatal.[70]

Alternative methods of treatment, more favoured because they were less intensive than Rush's standard, included gentle purging, blistering (as opposed to Rush's choice of venesection), and wrapping patients in vinegar-soaked blankets.[71] At the time of the 1804 yellow fever epidemic in Gibraltar, the Medical Officer of Health, Dr. Nooth, also advocated blood-letting. Other local remedies included a perspiration-based therapy involving bedrest, hot foot baths, and hot sugar drinks.[72]

Modern day scholars concur that physician treatments did not always benefit patients in the manner intended, for as Howard-Jones suggests some 19th century therapies were, at best, "a form of benevolent homicide".[73] A more charitable perspective is that of Worth Estes who believes that supportive care giving during the course of fever and dehydration may have proved beneficial,

> it is important to recall that we still have no treatment that selectively counteracts or inactivates the yellow fever virus. Only bed rest and supportive nursing care, along with symptomatic treatment of fever, pain and vomiting, and perhaps correction of electrolyte imbalances, can alleviate the illness.[74]

Those fortunate enough to receive care at home or in the hospital would have benefited enormously compared to those unfortunate souls who were simply left alone to deal with a critical period of high fever, malnourishment and dehydration.

Friday 31
This is a most beautiful morning and no more appearance of rain than if we were never to have any more. Took a boat and went along side the *Ann* from London for some Pounds of Beef Tongues Butter and Cheese which got and safely housed. The Captain was very much alarmed by my sending the order on board for fear of fever.   Died 20

November

Saturday 1
This day commences with a fine clear atmosphere and no appearance of rain whatever. the principal Medical Officer am sorry to say is very ill. In a general way there is nothing today very particular Died 12

Sunday 2
This morning after breakfast went up the Rock with Alexander our intention was to have gone to the battery on the North Front but from taking a wrong road we were discovered by the Artillery men who ordered us to come down upon pain of being fired at – we proceeded to the Signal House[33] accompanied by Miss Ettles and Blount. Whilst up we heard a very heavy saluting at Tangier supposed to be the Bomb-Ketch And Sloop of War lately at Algeciras. Died this morning Mr Nahon[34] a very rich Jew on the Neutral Ground. His shed put in Quarantine. Died 11

Monday 3
The consternation this morning is very great for the loss

The Problem of Diagnosis

The death of Mr. Nahon, as reported by our diarist, illustrates the problem associated with the accurate diagnosis of yellow fever, especially with its varying symptoms arising from varying degrees of severity, as well as biases stemming from the concurrence of raging epidemic. Thornton reports in his diary that on the morning of November 2nd 1828, Mr. Nahon -- a very rich Jew -- died on the Neutral Ground. His shed was immediately put in quarantine. The clear implication is that Nahon died of yellow fever, and more importantly he died of the fever even after having taking refuge on the Neutral Ground for some time.

However, there is evidence to suggest that Nahon did not in fact die of yellow fever. The picture that emerges is that Mr. Nahon, a Gibraltar landlord, along with his family (numbering seventeen) took shelter in a shed on the Neutral Ground in the early part of September. One would assume that such a measure would have put him and his family out of harm's way, given the salubrious environment of the area. After more careful diagnosis, it was reported three days later, by Hugh Fraser [along with Dr. Foote] that, "I do not consider the case to have been one of the prevailing epidemic fever, I should rather be inclined to view it as one of serious apoplexy, occurring in a subject naturally constituted of a gross, bloated, and phlegmatic temperament."[75] It was further reported that Nahon's vomit was not black, and the byproduct of medicines he had taken. The issue here reflects the very problem those infected with a poorly understood disease set within prevailing climate of fear and ignorance.

of Dr Hennan a man universally respected from his humane and fatherly conduct to almost every individual that came under his care. - He has not been married to the present- to any very great length of time by her he has only one child but several children grown up by a former marriage.

Mr Hyde the collector also died this morning. he has left a large family one son five daughters. All very helpless in fact I have been told by Dr S that although Mrs H has had such a family she absolutely does not know how to dress an infant. Died 15

Tuesday 4
This morning very fine and business a little improving. Miss G called this morning to purchase mourning for the family of the late Dr Hennan and in the course of conversation gave me to understand that for some time previous to his death he had not the slightest fever on him and frequently told Miss Hennan he should be up again in a day or so

From the commencement Dr Broadfoot has been very officious in offering his services which have always been declined by the former on the ground that they were quite unnecessary and that he had been able to sign the reports up to Sunday. But on the evening of that day the man servant unthinking brought a note into the room and gave to Miss H who immediately saw it was from Sir G Don and that it of course of an agreeable nature complied to his request of his reading it himself. In a few minutes he

'Passing Through the Fever'

After three encounters with yellow fever, the inhabitants of Gibraltar were comfortable with one unshakeable fact: those who had survived the fever would not be liable to a second attack. This truism was recognized early on when yellow fever struck in the autumn of 1813 and a resident physician observed, "It is an extraordinary fact that allegedly upwards of 3,000 persons are here who had the fever in 1804, not one instance had occurred of the above number having the present fever."[76] By the epidemic of 1828, efforts to gather information on those who had 'passed through the fever' represented the first step in a well-known strategy for combating epidemic outbreaks in Gibraltar.[77] Implementation of strategic action took place within days of the outbreak of the epidemic, as Dr. Hennen, PMO, instructed to the Inspectors of Districts,[78]

> to procure lists of all Persons who have passed through former Epidemics with a view that they may be permitted to remain in the Garrison. It being understood however that this permission is not to extend to such members of their families as not strictly within the meaning of this proposition.

Once the list was compiled, authorities removed the so-called 'unseasoned' to the Neutral Ground and allowed those who had passed through the fever to remain in the town. Those who had previously passed through an epidemic of yellow fever were issued a special ticket, which allowed for comparatively free movement throughout the territory.[79]

As Dr. Pym observed, Gibraltar's neighbours were similarly convinced the individuals who had passed through the fever were not liable to second attack:

> The Spaniards are so fully convinced that the infection cannot be communicated a second time, that a certificate of their having passed the disease is a sufficient passport through a cordon of troops into an infected town, which they enter without the smallest apprehension. [Y ademas se prohibió la entrada a los que no *manifestaban documentos* de haberla sufrido, poniendo a este fin guardias en las puertas, consultando por este medio con los sentimientos de humanidad en utilidad recíproca. Don Miguel Iribaren, Procurador Mayor][80]

he returned it to Miss H and said it was all very right and became very much irritated and restless at the same time. but still endeavoured to conceal it but alas to no purpose in an hour or two he was seized with a tremendous shivering which continued at intervals when one very severe relieved him from all his cares and troubles in this world.

The contents of this note so disagreeable in its nature and so distressing in its effects on his mind was nothing more or less than to say that the before mentioned Dr B[roadfoot] was to succeed and act as the Principal Medical Officer during this illness this stroke was so unexpected by him and particularly from the quarter whence it came that in all probability and in the opinion of Dr Fraser was the only and sole cause of his death. Died 17

Wednesday 5
This morning very fine and about 9 O'clock a vessel came into the bay from England and sent on shore two Medical gentlemen sent out by the British Government. But we are in hope please God their services will not be much required as the disease is abated a little. We are all most anxiously waiting for the rains. Died 20

Thursday 6
This morning The Packet sailed for England with a fine strong Easterly breeze a great quantity of letters. No doubt fine accounts will be received by many persons of the state of things going on in the Garrison. All deaths 17 Died 16

I certify, that *Juan Peña* of the *Catholic* Persuasion, aged *17* years, has passed the present Epidemic Fever.

J. D. Thurston

GIBRALTAR,
31. December, 1828.

A FEVER TICKET (GM)

Friday 7
This morning very dark and continues with very heavy clouds till about 2 O'clock when it began to rain and in a short time came down in torrents about 10 at night began Thundering and Lightning in an awful manner. Many of the tents on the Neutral Ground were blown away altogether and some of the Huts were removed with their Inhabitants to quite a different situation but the last not by the wind but were absolutely obliged to be removed on Mens shoulders.   All deaths 18   Died 15

Saturday 8
The rain continues at intervals very heavy but between the showers it is fine and pleasant towards the Evening. a Brig coming in saluted the Garrison which was returned of course she proved to be the Gun Brig Royalist from Plymouth in eleven days with a New Doctor General to the forces and three or four other Medical Men. A notice appears in the Chronicle to night that no persons are to pass Bay side Barrier. Died 9   The whole deaths in garrison today 17

Sunday 9
Still continues to rain and the Clouds from the SW are very black and heavy a great many vessels are moving about in the straights several came into the Bay in the Evening. there has been a great quantity of deals[35] sent to neutral grounds today to assist if possible in keeping the poor inmates of the tents from getting wet All deaths 12   Died 8

The Gibraltar Chronicle

During the yellow fever epidemics, there was only one local newspaper – the *Gibraltar Chronicle*. During any crisis, be it war or epidemic, this newspaper was the official source of information available to the public. Formal notification of the end of the epidemic, for example, were made known to the public in the *Chronicle*,

> His Excellency the Lieutenant Governor has the gratification to announce the termination of the Epidemic Fever which has lately afflicted this Community. … His Excellency also directs, that all internal measures of Quarantine shall cease on the 16th inst.; that the Courts of Justice and places of public resort be opened on the 17th; and Clean Bills of Health be issued from the Port on that day.[81]

In addition to posted proclamations and notices, the only official written word on the nature, cause and progress of the epidemic would be found in the pages of the *Chronicle*.[80] During the 1828 epidemic, it was the *Chronicle* which published daily statistics on the course of the disease; these are quoted by Thornton in his diary. To ensure that up to date and reliable counts of the sick and dying were made, Gibraltar's Principal Medical Officer, Dr. Hennen, ordered that,[82]

GIBRALTAR CHRONICLE
AND
COMMERCIAL INTELLIGENCER.

No. 2242. **FRIDAY, SEPTEMBER 12, 1828.**

All Public Acts appearing in this Chronicle, signed by the Proper Authorities, are to be considered as Official and obeyed as such.
By Command of His Excellency the LIEUT. GOVERNOR.
S. R. CHAPMAN, *Civil Secretary.*

Meteorological Observations, Sept. 11.
Hours. Barometer.—Thermom. Atmosphere.
In. 10ths. Degrees.

9 P.M.	29	9	74	SW.	clear.
12 Noon.	29	9	76¼	do.	do.
5 P.M.	29	9	77½	W.	do.

Fresh SW. during the day; latter part NW. and clear throughout.

Astronomical do., Sept. 12.
Fifth day of the Moon.

Sun rises at 5 h. 48 m. and sets at 6 h. 12 m.
High Water at Waterport 3 h. 27 m. P.M.

GIBRALTAR'S NEWSPAPER - THE CHRONICLE

Monday 10
An Article so singular in itself appearing in the Gibraltar Chronicle of this day cannot do less than copy it

"A recent discovery has been made by an English Physician which at the period must prove highly interesting to the Inhabitants and Garrison of Gibraltar that Light has the property of rendering altogether inert that matter which is the remote cause of yellow fever. This Gentleman states that people may during the day follow their ordinary occupation, but that, before sun set, they should retire to their houses which should be well lighted, and that no individual should retire to his chamber without having two reflecting tin lamps burning the whole night as long as the Epidemic Fever prevails. Should this be faithfully persisted in for three weeks no individual will be attacked with Fever after that period, although the cause should not be removed" Upon the whole there is not anything particular today All deaths 15 Died 11

Tuesday 11
This morning the wind is blowing pretty fresh and looks like a very unpleasant day. There are general papers posted up in the Garrison respecting the principal medical officer Dr B[roadfoot]. One of them as under

Wanted
For the public service
A principal medical officer. He must be a Man of sound practical ability - Must possess Common Sense and other requisites to qualify him for the important trust

The Civil Practitioners are again requested to send in their Reports daily to this Office by 8 o'clock, A.M. at latest.

It will be impossible for the General Report to be prepared, if this arrangement is not compiled with.

It is to be understood, that the Report is required daily from every individual, whether he may have patients or not.

Hennen's directive meant that readers of the *Chronicle* would be supplied with reliable and immediate information on the daily progress of the epidemic (see Table 6). One such account that appeared during the early part of the epidemic is reproduced below,[83]

The Febrile Diseases, which appear annually in this Garrison in the month of August, did not exhibit any thing peculiar towards the end of the month, when some suspicious cases were observed in District 24: up to the 31st of August, these Cases amounted to thirteen. Up to the 10th of September, the total number of Fevers of every species, from Heat, Intemperance, &c., have been 121, including civilians and military; 23 cases have proved fatal.

The following is the Morning State of yesterday

	Civil Hospital	Civilian Out Patients	Military Hospital	Total
Remained on the 10th Sept 1828	23	19	44	86
Admitted	6	19	5	30
Total	29	38	49	116
Discharged	5	2	1	8
Died	2	1	1	4
Remaining on the 11th Sept 1828	22	35	47	104
Remarks				
Serious	12	14	5	31
Slight	1	14	36	51
Convalescent	9	7	6	22

TABLE 6. DAILY REPORT OF THE CASES OF FEVER OF THE MILITARY AND CIVIL POPULATION, GIBRALTAR, 11TH SEPTEMBER, 1828.[84]

Apply by letter to
A Bullicugie Md
Inspector of Hospitals ad interim
NB
Left handed men not approved of Died 15

Wednesday 12
The public mind appears to be greatly irritated against Dr Broadfoot for his orders counterorders etc. such as ordering the Communication between the Garrison and Neutral Ground to be suspended and then on the next day to be opened again. Such like and these inconsistencies at this stage has raised the indignation of all most all parties against him. Another paper posted up this morning runs thus Wanted a Skilfull Barber to shave the head of the Inspector of health, apply a Cataplasm and administer Clyster. Died this morning Mary Ann Hyde 2nd daughter and Lucy 3rd daughter of Mr Hyde also Lieut Williamson 73 Regiment All deaths including omissions of yesterday 26 Died 12

Thursday 13
This morning tolerably fine with the Sun to enliven us a little. Persons generally speaking seem to be pleased with the appearance of the Fevers decreasing as the admissions from the reports are only 25 and discharges 51. His Excellency the Lieutenant Governor has been pleased to appoint Mr James Terry to be collector of the different Rates of this Garrison. vice Mr W Hyde deceased All deaths 9 Died 7

Inspector's Office, 11th Sept., 1828.
          (signed)   J. Hennen
                    Inspector of Hospitals

Mem. –   1 child of Infantile Fever
          1 of Convulsions
          2   died on the Neutral Ground.
          S.R. Chapman, Civil Secretary

The *Chronicle* also served as one of the primary means by which to issue directives to the local doctors,[85]

> Such Civil Practitioners as many have Patients under their treatment in their own Dwellings, must henceforth keep them there, and not send them into the Civil Hospital. Should it, however, in any urgent case, be thought desirable by the Civil Practitioners, to send Patients to the said Institution, it must be done within the first 24 hours; and they must send, along with them, details of the cases and of the previous treatment ....

By publishing such accounts, Gibraltar's inhabitants were not only kept informed of what measures being taken, but also that authorities remained proactive in combating the disease. In a similar vein, the Chronicle kept its readers posted on international events that could potentially impact on health of the garrison. One such article that appeared in the *Chronicle* before the outbreak of the Gibraltar epidemic reported on the health of Havana,[86] the probable source of yellow fever infection for much of Iberian peninsula,

> ... letters from the Havannah, of the 14th June, contain a certificate from three physicians, that yellow fever, which had existed in the spring of the year, has entirely subsided, and the harbour is, comparatively speaking, healthy, more so than it has been for years in this season...[87]

At this time the *Chronicle* was also the only forum through which foreign articles on the nature of yellow fever or other infectious epidemic diseases could be republished for local consumption.[88]

The *Chronicle* also fulfilled one final significant function during the epidemic as the medium by which pleas for support and charity could reach the public. Calls for aid from the "humane Public" for "helpless families now encamped on the Neutral Ground" appeared as early as two weeks after the

Doctor Chervin, so well known by his many important labours in the cause of humanity as well as that of science, has been appointed by the Royal Academy of Medicine to proceed to Gibraltar to study and attempt to counteract, the yellow fever. Paris Oct 29.

Friday 14
This morning the weather looks very heavy and dark very like rain which about the middle of the day came down in torrents and continued almost the whole night with Lightning and Thunder. All deaths 11 Died 8

Saturday 15
There has been scarce anything worth notice in any way or shape to day, but the public opinion is now generally that the fever will gradually leave us which I sincerely hope will be the case the rain has continued at intervals the whole day. All deaths 14 Died 8

Sunday 16
This morning tolerably fine and at first had the appearance of continuing, but began raining again towards evening which continued the whole night almost without ceasing. All deaths 13 Died 2

Monday 17
Still continues raining. the general opinion is that the weather will by the latter end of this month. please God clear us from the dreadful scourge of mankind which will turn out no doubt much worse than any since 1804. All deaths 12 Died 10

outbreak of the epidemic.[89] The Chronicle also informed the public of those who contributed to these charities listing the amount and name of a donor. On a more morbid level. it also posted advertisements for the selling the effects of dead officers.

Remembering the Military Dead

The military response to any crisis situation is universally shaped by its inherent qualities of discipline, rank and order. The two published accounts reproduced below capture these values and speak to the military response to death and epidemics.[90]

The 1828 Yellow Fever Epidemic

Died
Royal Engineers – Lieut. Bull
Royal Artillery – Lieut.-Colonel Payne
12th Foot – Lieut. Werge, Lieut. Forsteen
42nd Foot – Ensign Stewart
73rd Foot – Lieut. Williamson, Assistant-Surgeon Fraser
94th Foot – Lieut. Osborne, Lieut. Alexander
Inspector of Hospitals and Principal Medical Officer – Dr. Hennen
Garrison Chaplain – W. Hatchman
Ordinance Storekeeper – Mr. Walrend

Severely, But Recovered
Royal Engineers – Capt. Fenwick
Royal Artillery – Major Gilmour, Capt. Bisset, Capt. Evans, Lieut. Burrows, Lieut. McCoy
12th Foot – Lieut. Strike
23rd Fusileers – Lieut. Philpott, Lieut. Powell, Lieut. Lawrence, Lieut. Hon. H. Stanley
42nd Foot – Major Malcolm, Capt. W. Murray, Lieut. Dun. Cameron
43rd Foot – Capt. S. Tryon, Lieut. and Adjt. Harris, Lieut. Hon. W.S. Clements, Lieut. Bryan, Lieut. Hon. A.A. Spencer
73rd Foot – Capt. Anstruther, Capt. Godfrey, Lieut. Widdrington, Lieut. Brown, Ensign M. O'Connell

Tuesday 18
There is now scarce anything going on in the garrison to amuse the public mind[36] now that everyone begins to forget the fever. There was another paper posted up this morning as below

From an Evening Journal London 32 Oct
We understand from good authority that Old Tom Walker has been appointed to supercede the present lieutenant governor of a certain Rocky Fortress. It is rumored that the prudent distribution of places and employment by him or rather by the Cabal that directs him has been the main cause of his removal.

We approve and rejoice in the adoption of this measure certain as we are that the public will not be losers by the exchange of heads. All deaths 12 Died 6

Wednesday 19
This day there is nothing of the least consequence either to be seen or heard with the exception of almost every person you speak to answering thank God the fever has almost left us. There has been a report in circulation that Our friend the King of Spain places the Inhabitants of this Garrison in Quarantine for 90 days after all the fever ceases if this be true we ought to be much obliged. Died 7

Thursday 20
This morning tolerably fine and rather cold. The appearance of the Straits from the Line Wall very winterly.

94th Foot – Major P.F. Thorne, Lieut. Mills, Lieut. Tullock, Lieut. Pipon
Assist.-Surgeon Woods
Asst. Com. Gen. F.E. Knowles
Dep. Asst. Com. Gen. – Spencer
Hosp. Asst. – W. Cruikshank
Hosp. Asst. – R. Laing
Garrison Quarter-Master – Gilchrist

The Soldier's Cemetery at Gibraltar[91]

Where the gaunt Rock o'er ocean throws
A strange supernatural shade,
Hard by its base in deep repose
Are laurell'd legions laid;
Cold is each heart and busy head;
O'er them no death-bell rings;
Few sculptures mark each low, lone bed;
The brave ask nobler things!

And seas, which raving lash the shore;
Gales round the rock which sweep;
Cannon from cloudy clefts, whose roar
Astounds the thund'ring deep-
Wail them with knell and minstrelsy
Sublime; their deeds declare;
Honour their last home awfully;-
Oh! Would that *I* slept there!

A Soldier Succumbs to the Fever, Trafalgar Cemetary

109

Sailed this American ship *Fanny* Capt Engle for Valparciso and Lima after having been waiting in this Port for freight very near six months. Mr Fraser assistant Surgeon 73 Regiment died this morning. I have been given to understand he had passed the fever but wishing to ascertain if a person could take it twice. Actually went to bed on the same that another officer had died on and it unfortunately proved fatal. Those of the Artillery that have passed the fever came back to their barracks this morning. All deaths 9 Died 5

Friday 21
This is a very fine morning and has continued the whole of the day every person looking anxiously for the Packet from England due yesterday. it is generally expected she will bring some money for the Poor in the Encampment at a meeting of the Committee some few days since it was announced that Subscriptions[37] in London amounted to 1700 Pounds and in Scotland to 2000 Pounds which will be very acceptable and reflect additional credit on our Countrymen at home. All deaths 5 Died 5

Saturday 22
This is a very black unpleasant looking morning which has continued the whole day. The Dispatch Capt E.M. Wallis sailed for Bahia etc. This afternoon about 3 O'clock with Mrs Wallis and family accompanied by one of the Miss Llewellyns. I saw Cap W. on the Wharf and think never saw him look bitter. He was busy shipping a very fine Maltese Donkey a commission from Bahia. There has nothing particular transpired today. Died 6

Diseases of Locality and Gibraltar's Weather

Nineteenth century physicians and the public often viewed weather condi-tions as the cause, or at least the catalyst, for poor health.[92] Non-contagion-ists (localists), in particular, concerned themselves with identifying features of the air that signified increases in heat, moisture, and decomposition. All of these fell under the general umbrella of conditions conducive to the develop-ment of disease-bearing miasmata. While few scholars today would attribute epidemic disease directly to local weather conditions, most would agree that meteorological factors are important background ecological mediators that can affect the well-being of humans.[93]

Historically, rainfall has been the climatic feature of the greatest concern in the Spanish Mediterranean region, due to its typical manifestation as a de-ficient resource, sometimes over long periods of time. Aside from periodic yearly shortages, there was the ever-present summer drought in Gibraltar when virtually not a single drop of water fell from the heavens. In more tech-nical terms, after the rains of November through March there was typically a long period of drought lasting from June to August, where the mean amount of rainfall in any of these months seldom exceeded a mere 12mm.[94] Exacer-bating the stress arising from this seasonal shortage of water was the inevi-table rise in temperature and humidity during the summer months. From a bio-meteorological perspective, the summer months (June, July, and August) were potentially very stressful, not only because of the lack of potable water, but also because of high temperatures and humidity levels. The sporadic ap-pearance of epidemics like yellow fever[95] during the summer months served to reinforce the perception that local weather could facilitate the development and spread of deadly diseases. For example, R. Amiel, Surgeon of the 12th Regiment stationed on the Rock, was convinced that yellow fever was propa-gated by impure air.

One of the major sources of 'impure air' in Gibraltar has been the Levant-er. Traditionally, the Levanter has been blamed for many ills, and there is no doubt that the dank, dark cloud contributes to irritability and depression amongst those who live under its shadow. Gibraltar lies in a North-South direction. The prevailing winds in the Straits are the West wind (often South-West) – *el poniente* – which often brings rainstorms in the winter, and the East

fine Maltese Donkey a commission from Bahia. There has nothing particular transpired today. Died 6

Sunday 23
The whole of this day has been very black and has had the appearance of rain but which has kept off till might when it rained hard for about 1/4 of an hour. the packet boat returned from Tangier to day not being allowed to have communication with the shore. - went for a walk round the encampment before dinner saw Mr and Mrs Cowel, Mrs T Duffield etc etc. All deaths 9 Died 4

The funeral of the late Mr Eshuzier took place this Evening. Attended by a number of very respectable persons. This Gentleman had been ill for some considerable time and has been reported dead three or four several times previous.

Monday 24
This morning very black and cloudy with the wind inclining to veer northward which made it really cold. There has been nothing of note today a proclamation appeared in the Chronicle this Evening as under

Whereas it has been officially announced to me by Commander David Hope, Senior Officer of his Majestys Ships of War in the Bay of Tangier that in consequences of the refusal of the Emperor of Morocco to accede to the just demands of His Majesty, Commander Hope had, pursuant to his instructions, put the Port of Tangier into a state of Blockade; I do, therefore, hereby publicly notify the est-

wind – *el levante* – anglicized to "Levanter", which on hitting the Rock at right angles, rises and cools, forming a dense cloud of condensation that clings to the Rock, and makes the atmosphere in the town muggy and unpleasant. Many authors noted this phenomenon, including Dr. Hennen himself, who stated in his book *The Medical Topography of the Mediterranean*: "By some, the approach of a Levanter can be announced before it reaches the hill, and there are few whose diseases or infirmities are not aggravated by its presence." The diarist mentions on several occasions his belief that the dark clouds and heavy weather were prejudicial to the fever. However, the Levanter was probably responsible for a beneficial phenomenon, which both doctors and inhabitants alike noted: No person who moved to the Neutral Ground, or to Europa suffered an attack of yellow fever. This could not be explained, given the state of medical knowledge at the time, but it seems clear that the strong winds swirling around the Rock, effectively "imprisoned" the *Aedes aegypti* mosquito within the Town area, making the North and South safe from the epidemic.

The Source

Since the epidemic of 1814, local records indicate that over eight hundred ships from different yellow fever countries had entered the harbour of Gibraltar, and yet, it was only 1828 until circumstances were ideal for another outbreak. While evidence of the source of the epidemic remains unclear, there are many who believe that the Swedish registered ship Dygden played a primary role as the source of importation.[96]

The Dygden left Havana on May 12th. The Caribbean and particularly Havana was regarded as 'the hot bed' of yellow fever, and for many a European the "White Man's Grave".[97] As you will recall, port cities in the Caribbean served as endemic centres for yellow fever and, through commerce, facilitated the spread of the dreaded yellow jack. The Dygden reached Gibraltar on the 28th of June. She was immediately placed in quarantine upon arrival since her bill of health (Patente) was judged unacceptable, owing to the fact that dengue fever was raging in Havana at the time of the ships departure. Gibraltar's local physician, Dr. Broadfoot, acknowledged the importance of the Dygden in the Proceedings of the Commission on the origin of the fever in Gibraltar stating emphatically, "… if that ship [the Dygden] was not the sole source, she was the principal means of bringing the

ablishment of the blockade of the Port of Tangier, and that the same will be maintained and enforced in the most affective manner. G Don, General Lieutenant Governor. All deaths 5 Died 2

Tuesday 25
There is a report in circulation this morning said to be from the French Medical Men who came into the garrison on Sunday last from Paris and sent by the French Government. It appears to be the opinion of these Gentlemen that the Fever we have been visited with originates in the Garrison and that it arises from many causes such as the hot weather atmosphere, crowded population, the drains dirty filth etc etc. If this turns out to be the case a number of people will be much mistaken and I think in a short time good bye to the trade of Gibraltar. Died 5

Wednesday 26
It has blown a very heavy gale of Wind all last night and the early part of this morning and has continued in intervals all day.

A few evenings since a very fine handsome Young Man a corporal in the 43 Regiment being it is supposed intoxicated unfortunately passed the Cordon and was hailed by the Spanish Sentrys and desired to go back but without effect. he either not understanding or not caring to understand kept on when he was fired upon and sorry to say was wounded in both legs he has had one amputated and it is feared he must also lose the other they they fired five shots but it is thought that they fired low on purpose to fever into the garrison." The ship remained in the harbour until free communication with shore (Pratique) was permitted on the 6th of August. Despite the Dygden's questionable health status, contact with the ship, its crew, and cargo occurred with the boarding of local sanitary guards. Dr. Broadfoot was firm in his belief that five of the ship's crew died of yellow fever in Havana, and two on her passage to Gibraltar. A further nine members of the crew had been sick during the long passage, and the mate of the ship was ill around the 24th while in quarantine. This critical fact was not reported to the local Inspector of Health. The Dygden's cargo of coffee and sugar was brought ashore during July.

As a potential means transmitting the disease to the local inhabitants, there is evidence to suggest human contact may have played a role. One of the sanitary guards [Francis Testa] was the brother of Mary Testa, according to some, one of the first Gibraltarians who contracted yellow fever. As a sanitary guard, it was his duty to board and remain onboard ships entering the port that local authorities wished to place under sanitary surveillance. Records indicate that Francis boarded the Dygden on 27th July. He slept on board the ship and

GIBRALTAR FROM THE SEA (GM)

115

bring him done or they must have killed him. All deaths 5
Died 3

Thursday 27
This morning arrived H M.Cutter Bramble Lieutenant
Haswell 25 days from Plymouth and 4 from Cadiz bringing
a reinforcement of 8 Medicals. Amongst them Dr. Dicks[38]
etc etc. it is to be hoped now we shall soon have more Doctors than Patients. How that will be God only knows. I am
extremely sorry this morning upon hearing of the Death
of that fine smart Young Officer Lieut Forsteen 12 Regiment[39] and believe he is sincerely regretted by all who
knew him and when spoken to about the fever always had
such spirits. it was just fifty hours from his being taken
told he was a corpse Died 6

Friday 28
Came into the Bay this morning H.M. Packet Tyrian Lieutenant Drwyer 18 days from Falmouth and 2 from Cadiz.
Passengers, Dr. Pym for this place and Sir T. Paisley R.N.
for Malta. There is very little variation in anything to
day am sorry to announce the Death of one of the Miss
Chathams of a relapse. She was to all appearance a very
nice pleasant genteel girl. Alas like many other nice girls -
she is gone. All deaths 5 Died 2

Saturday 29
This morning arived H.M. Packet Plover, Lieutenant
from Corfu and 7 from Malta. Passengers Miss Casson and
Pye for Gibraltar. The fever still goes on we are in hopes
decreasing but it is thought to decrease less rapid this

returned to his sister's home and family on the 6th of August. Upon return-ing to his sister's, he took with him his bedding, blanket, and soiled clothing. There is some evidence to suggest that even the Captain of Dygden himself visited Mary Testa on 13th August. There is a possibility that he also became ill with the fever on the 9th of September. It was reported that the clothes of the men who died on board the ship were sold to the sailors that landed aboard the ship. To complicate matters further, there were other ships in the harbour prior to the outbreak of yellow fever epidemic in Gibraltar. One of these was the Meta, another ship that departed from Havana. Since these ships left port before the Commission could examine the health status of the ships and their crew, any definitive conclusions regarding the source of the infection will remain indeterminate.

Sou and Yellow Fever

By the end of the 18th century, Gibraltar was transformed from a small military garrison town into a bustling "grand emporium"[98] drawing thousands of im-migrants from abroad. Seeking political refuge, steady employment, higher wages, or the opportunity to make large and quick fortunes, a vast number of foreigners entered the fortress gates daily. [99] Gibraltar began to benefit not only from its status as an international port, entrepôt centre and financial mar-ketplace, but also from the considerable outlays of the British Admiralty which was headquartered there.[100] Whether through legal or suspicious means, the flow of goods in and out of Gibraltar meant great wealth and quick profits in, as Barry remarked, "a free port as Gibraltar, where everything is admitted indiscriminately, where smuggling outwards is encouraged, and indeed the very soul of its trade."[101] One of the hallmarks of early 19th century Gibraltar was the influx of "seedy adventurers" who were attracted by the allure of an open Mediterranean port. [102] A great number of these adventurers were en-gaged in the highly profitable activity of smuggling with reports of,

> ...a fleet of 73 sail of armed vessels, manned by some of the most daring and reck-less of the desperadoes of the Mediterranean...The number of men must be at least 1500 and the tonnage 4000, and as the voyages are generally short, that to Málaga being frequently no more than 24 hrs, it should seem that in this particular they could dispose of a very large portion of the produce of Manchester itself, if purchasers could be found.[103]

The spoils of privateers not only benefited Gibraltar's mercantile community,

time than any times previous most years previous. It has generally finish by the end of this month at least so I am given to understand. *All deaths 6 Died 3*

Sunday 30

This morning rather showery however managed to walk to the Encampment and paid a short visit to Mr and Mrs Payton. The latter have not seen for some months they are now all very well although both have suffered from the fever but the children escaped. – There has been a great rejoicing at the Office of the Principal Medical Officer upon Dr Pym's being appointed to succeed the late bright Luminary Dr Broadfoot. It was reported there was to be an illumination in consequence. *Died 3*

December

Monday 1

Am very sorry to hear that our friend Col. Payne is down with fever and his case is considered serious. it is almost wonderful how he has lasted till this time. for he was walking about generally the greatest part of the day. Understand Lieut Coutchley 23 Regiment was relieved from guard to day and is reported a serious case. Am sorry the packet could not get out today *All deaths 6 Died 4*

Tuesday 2

This morning very fine and the Sun really very hot. A Spanish Cavalry Officer came to the Neutral Ground through the Cordon accompanied by a Young Lady who reports say has eloped with him in consequence of his

but even the community at large. As Governor O'Hara remarked,

> Although I am by no means partial to Privateers, I must acknowledge that the Garrison and the Inhabitants have derived great advantage in receiving many necessary comforts of life through their means particularly by Cargoes of Flour, Sugar and Wine, the latter was very essential to the health of the Troops under the laborious Duties in the Garrison.[104]

The economic benefits of smuggling were not confined to the inhabitants of Gibraltar, as there were great profits to be made by those participating in the illicit tobacco trade in Spain. The magnitude of this prohibited trade during the early 19th century was staggering,

> The proof of the extent to which his [the tobacco smuggler's] dealing are carried was exemplified in 1828, when many thousand additional hands were obliged to be put on the manufactories at Seville and Granada, to meet the increased demand occasioned by the impossibility of obtaining supplies from Gibraltar, in consequence of the yellow fever which was then raging there.[105]

It is clear that the interruption of trade during epidemic times rippled well beyond the local confines of Gibraltar.

The lawlessness of the privateer, however, did not always benefit the population, despite the importation of desirable goods. It was not uncommon for such individuals to break quarantine and place the community-at-large at risk for disease. Such was the case in 1804 when authorities suspected that smugglers from Cádiz and Málaga had introduced the disease into Gibraltar.[106] In the aftermath of the 1828 epidemic, claims of a laxity in the policing of immigrants to Gibraltar rose to the surface,

> The department of the police, which regulates the admission of strangers, is entirely composed of foreigners who are notoriously remiss in their performance of duties. Nothing was more easy than to elude the vigilance of the "Inspector of Strangers" and hundreds may, I have heard it stated by respectable persons, that even thousands have entered the fortress in this manner, without "permits" and have resided there undetected…

The perception of a general lack of control over the settling of immigrants in Gibraltar went hand-in-hand with concerns over the silent and swift introduction of diseases into the town.

Colonel's not allowing him to marry her.

Arrived this morning H.M. Brig Britmart Capt Manners from a Cruise also H.M. Ship Meteor, Capt Hope 6 hours from Tangier and a Dutch Transport from Rotterdam with Troops and provisions for Batavia in 41 days lost his rudder in a gale of wind on 5 Nov Lat 57 Long 21.51W, put into get a new one. All deaths 4 Died 1

Wednesday 3
This morning anything but pleasant nasty black heavy clouds hanging over the rock which makes it damp cold and very unhealthy particularly for those poor creatures that are recovering from the fever various opinions upon. The decrease of the disease there are certainly more admission this morning then yesterday and more deaths am really grieved to say Col Payne is worse today. All deaths 6 Died 4

Thursday 4
This is a very fine morning and things seem to partake of the appearance of the weather for when it is dull almost all people look and speak dull particularly at such times as there in speaking to a person on a dark cloudy morning. Their ideas are generally cloudy and such as I think we shall never get rid of this fever and what disagreeable weather etc etc. but on a fine bright morning how different. It is when they say well we shall now surely get rid of the fever what beautiful weather etc etc. I am sorry to say Our Old friend Col Payne R.A. And I might say everybody's friend for am persuaded he was a good man Died

The French Commissioners

Dr. Chervin, Dr. Louis, and Dr. Trousseau were three eminent French physicians who were sent to Gibraltar in 1828 by the Académie de Médecine of Paris to try to establish the causes of the yellow fever epidemic. Trousseau and Chervin were respectively for and against the contagiousness of yellow fever, and Louis was appointed by the Academie as a 'neutral' commissioner, at the request of the French Ministry of the Interior.

Nicholas Chervin (1783-1843) qualified in Paris in 1812, and soon after, went to North America and the Caribbean, where he studied yellow fever. He returned to Europe in 1822, and his systematic study of the yellow fever epidemic of that year in Barcelona clearly demonstrated that contagion could not have played a part in the spread of the epidemic. He was also convinced that yellow fever was an endemic disease and was not imported. He was the only one of the commissioners to have had extensive first-hand experience with yellow fever.

Pierre Charles Alexandre Louis (1787-1872) was a distinguished French physician and pathological anatomist at l'Hôpital de la Charité. He wrote extensively on tuberculosis, and was one of the first to use statistical methods in the study of disease. He wrote a detailed account of his studies on the symptoms, signs, and morbid anatomy of patients in Gibraltar with yellow fever, but did not commit himself as to the causes of the epidemic.

Armand Trousseau (1801-1867) qualified in Paris in 1822, where he was a pupil of Pierre Bretonneau. His grounding in Bretonneau's biological view of communicable disease might have suggested that he was a hard-line contagionist, but his views were in fact more balanced. He made no public comment about the epidemic until 1857, when he contested Chervin's description of Gibraltar as marshy, and therefore liable to morbid miasmas.

this evening. universally lamented by his brother officers and friends it is really very dreadful when you think that this gentlemen with his family ought to have returned to England six months since and had Sold off part of his furniture that he might be in readiness to go at the moment his successor should arrive which from interest or some other motive had been prevented from time to time or having heard of the fever raging here had wisely declined coming at present and unfortunately lost this poor Gentleman's life to the regret of his family and friends. I have heard that he fortunately disposed of his commission two days previous to his death and that it was signed by Sir G. Don. Supposed to be worth 4500 Pounds or more which will be no doubt a good thing for his family. All deaths 8 Died 9

Friday 5
This morning the remains of the much lamented Col Payne were consigned to the Tomb at the Sand Pitts attended only by a few of his brother officers there has been nothing of consequence today All deaths 5 Died 1

Saturday 6
This morning was seized with a violent pain on all my right side but managed to come down eat a short breakfast. When I went to bed again found myself so cold that could not possibly get warm or lie still. Maria came and very kindly laid three extra blankets upon me and yet it was some time more than an hour before I found any warmth from there Mr Wearing came up soon after when he thought it advisable to send for a doctor. has accordingly sent for Dr Sewell who when he came pronounced

Dr. William Pym

William Pym[107] (1772-1861) was born in Edinburgh, and graduated from the University in Edinburgh. He joined the medical department of the army after serving for a short time in the Navy. He served in the West Indies in 1794, when a severe outbreak of yellow fever spread among the regiments. This epidemic lasted for three years; 16,000 troops died. Pym thus obtained unparalleled first-hand knowledge of the disease, and his fixed opinion that the disease was contagious, as well as imported. Upon his return to Europe, he heard that yellow fever had appeared in Gibraltar in 1804, and he immediately made his way there. Finding Gibraltar's the senior medical officer, Dr Nooth (a non-contagionist), debilitated following an attack of the fever, Pym took over in his place. In 1810, he was again in Gibraltar, when several cases of yellow fever emerged. The disease did not reach epidemic proportions, and Pym attributed this to the measures of quarantine and isolation that he instituted.[108,109]

In 1828, he again made his way to Gibraltar, arriving two months after the start of the epidemic and on the day following the death of the Principal Medical Officer, Dr Hennen. Pym recorded "although I had gone to Gibraltar to superintend and give directions in a civil capacity, the Lieutenant-Governor insisted upon my taking charge of the military medical department of the garrison." After the epidemic was over, Pym was appointed Chairman of a Board of Inquiry.[110] The Board, no doubt heavily influenced by Pym, concluded that the yellow fever was a distinct disease from the locally prevalent summer fevers, and was contagious as well as imported. Suspicions fell on the Swedish ship Dygden, which had arrived from Havana on the 28th of June. It was also agreed (correctly) that an attack of yellow fever provided lasting immunity to a second attack.

it a slight attack of fever well then the next thing was medicine- the first thing was a powder which had no effect the next 2 oz of castor oil with as little effect at night 2 oz more no sleep all night
All deaths 6 Died 3

Sunday 7
Sunday morning felt worse but no fever another powder which affected me with sickness etc etc. continued ill all day at night 3 pills and another powder and Maria kindly sat up all night with me as she did most of Saturday night.[41] no sleep and found myself in a great deal of pain Monday morning called the doctor in early who found me very ill from the medicine. I had taken and none of them had operated as was intended he directly went for a Spanish Barber to administer Clysters to me. at this time he gave me two which relieved me from the pain at the bottom of my stomach about noon took another powder and in the evening had two more clysters-

This morning I was certainly very bad in fact so bad that I thought should not recover but God Almighty is more good to me than I deserve. All deaths 6 Died 1

Tuesday 9
This morning thank God. Am much better although at times feel a great deal of pain. This evening two ounces more Castor Oil. Think if this continues long shall become more expert at taking medicine than had given myself credit for. All deaths 5 Died 2

Fear, Grief, and Disease

Psychological factors could also have affected the outcome and contributed to the reason why some individuals succumbed to the disease and others escaped death. Fear, in particular, was often cited as an important factor in the deadly equation of life and death during an epidemic. It was not uncommon even among physicians and health authorities to share a similar belief. For example, W.W. Fraser, Principal Medical Officer in Gibraltar from 1814 to 1825, commenting on yellow fever in 1813 and 1814, thought that mental affection or "fear, as it is vulgarly termed," might be a precipitating factor.[111] Watts has described this attitude as "rather muddled Gaelic understandings," according to which the "non-natural mental state known as melancholy or depression" was a predisposing factor in, or effective cause of, pestilential disease.[112] A physician practicing at the time of the 1828 yellow fever visitation put it this way:

> impure air is the primary and essential cause of the disease [yellow fever]. ... I consider as secondary causes, mental depression, exposure to heat, cold, fear, intemperance, anxiety, &c. which in some individuals, have brought on an immediate attack of the epidemic fever; while others, by carefully avoiding these exciting causes, have been uninfluenced by the noxiousness of the atmosphere, and escaped the disease.[113]

The idea of fear as an influential factor on yellow fever susceptibility was not new nor was it confined to Gibraltar. A letter by Assistant Surgeon Clarke which appeared in the medical journal Lancet on the subject of fear as 'an exciting cause' of disease offered the following 'proof',

> ...the death of a person received from a vessel having yellow fever on board, excited very great alarm amongst the crew hitherto very healthy, fitting their bodies for the receipt of the miasma generated in the floating marsh over which they lived. The content and cheerfulness consequent on the total cessation of fever after the removing cause, gives countenance to the idea.[114]

Such sentiments continued to be heard throughout the 19th century as Gibraltar was to be further devastated by a series of other epidemics.[115]

Similar beliefs in the role of fear in disease causation existed elsewhere. For example, in examining diaries and letters of those who experienced the 1793 yellow fever epidemic in Philadelphia, Miller also finds that unbridled fear was

Wednesday 10
Am better this morning but tremendously hungry. If they do not give me something to eat soon shall get up and go and look for something. Thank God Almighty this is the first time I have been three days confined to my bed in my whole life that I recollect.   All deaths 3 Died 1

Thursday 11
This morning received a letter from my little friend Dick now St Roque with which I was much pleased. The little fellow seems anxious to see me again he says he longs to be seated next me at table again. When he was here we certainly used to have great fun with him when he will be here again God only knows. Came downstairs to day.   Died 7

Friday 12
Came down to the dining room again this morning and feel now quite myself and to my great joy the Doctor allows me to eat meat to day for the first time since this attack. Look forward with anxiety for the dinner hour that I may appease my appetite with some beef etc etc. All deaths 7 Died 2

Saturday 13
This a very disagreeable morning with great many large black clouds hanging over the rock which makes it damp and unpleasant. Myself thank God feel quite well but am anxious to breathe the fresh air, have not heard anything of the least consequence today.
All deaths 13 Died 1

one emotion that physicians warned needed to be controlled to survive the epidemic.[116] The ability to avoid or contain fear and the belief that fate "was in God's hands" were two of the central premises that allowed Philadelphians to carry on during the epidemic. Miller also examines another emotion, namely grief, and the general acceptance of the notion "that grief weakened the body's resistance to disease"; often the avoidance of grief led to the appearance of a stoic and seemingly resigned acceptance of the death of a loved one.[117] In general, middle-class Philadelphians placed great value on emotional self-control, believing that a strict governing of passions would help to maintain good health in times of extreme crisis. Mortality statistics collected at the time of the 1793 epidemic seemed to confirm, for the middle class, that their emotional self-control was effective since a large proportion of deaths occurred amongst the lower- class, a social group which, as a whole, was believed to be incapable of controlling their emotions with the same level of finesse and restraint (overlooking, of course, the greater likelihood that the poor were undernourished and lived in overcrowded and rundown dwellings).

In Philadelphia, Miller notes that to preserve the relative peace experienced with the belief that divine Providence was guiding the epidemic, some Philadelphians rejected standard practices, such as the air-purifying tar and tobacco burning favoured by those who feared miasmas. To undertake this active measure would seemingly contradict their faith.[118] Chalhoub found that in the midst of the 1849-1850 yellow fever epidemic in Rio de Janeiro, Brazil, some of the city's inhabitants felt "that church bells should not toll announcing deaths during an epidemic because people would be depressed and more susceptible to disease."[119]

Sunday 14

To day thank God am once more allowed to walk out and have been round the Alamada[42] and walking theather met with her cousin Alexander both of whom were surprised that I should be out walking; as was likewise Dr Thurston who told me if I had been a patient of his he would have marched me home with a file of the guard. I do not know when I have enjoyed anything so much as this walk for everything appeared new and the Alamada beautiful and green. it almost appeared as if I had risen from the dead. Died 2 7

Monday 15

This morning have descended again to the Shop where I received the congratulations of many persons scarcely could have known me or have known that I had been ill even but as it is I hope please God none of them may be mistaken as to my having passed the fever and to have passed it so slight. All deaths 6 Died 2

Tuesday 16

From having exerted myself so much yesterday find myself not quite so well to day as I thought. I have great weakness in my back etc. Took a walk to the Alamada this morning and when had returned found myself quite tired. Saw a very Large Ship entering the Straits and supposed her to be one of the Line of Battle ships ordered for this place with troops etc. All deaths 3 Died 1

Wednesday 17

This is a very fine morning unfortunately for us here

Dr. Hennen Falls Victim to the Fever

On October 28th, Dr. John Hennen fell ill and although he forced himself to carry on working almost until the end, he succumbed to the yellow fever on November 3rd, 1828, at the age of 49.[120] Writing of her father's death, A.M. Hennen[121] describes her father's last mortal moments,

> … for two months preceding His death, he went thro labour which might fully employed six persons. The day was spent in laborious exertions out of doors, with scarce intervals long enough to take the support he so much needed … He invariably rose about midnight, and worked until dawn, when he called for coffee, and then began the business of the day. He bore all this wonderfully and except at times when he seemed nearly exhausted, looked well as usual but this was not at all, after His attack he would not allow himself to be reported sick but continued to do the office business, and was to within a few hours of His Death, supported in Bed to sign and dictate official papers.

> …. After hours of dreadful agitation, he seemed at four in the morning some what composed, after giving him some nourishment, I lay down and hearing him quiet - she dozed.

> When the sound of a sudden and most violent effort to vomit made me start to the bedside, before I reached it, a convulsion which shook Him, agitated his whole frame, and when I raised his head which in the attempt to vomit He had learnt over the Bed, he had ceased to breath - I sent for assistance. …

> The last words he said were " If I could keep quiet a day or two, I should be well", but he could not keep quiet, his mind was in a state of anxiety which nothing could remove. The Duty of the Office were ever in His Mouth or in His thoughts...

His loss was felt by all in Gibraltar and a memorial to his courage and contribution to the people of Gibraltar remains in the King's Chapel.

so far as respect the decrease of this dreadful disease. I am really very sorry to say that there are 9 admissions to day to the hospitals which there is never an instance of such a number of fresh cases at this late season of the year. God only knows if we shall loose it all this Year or next. All deaths 3 Died 2

Thursday 18
The whole of this day we have all been very busy receiving opening and marking all the different Good that we have at past received from the Steam Packet[43] which vessel ought to have landed them when she touched have now nearly two months since and as all the goods were for winter. The loss will fall heavy upon some person or other. The captain gives as his reason for not landing them the receipt of a letter at Portmouth from his owners that it was useless to touch at Cadiz or Gibraltar as both those places were strictly blockaded. Died 1

Friday 19
This morning tolerably fine and towards the middle of the day quite hot which of course makes it so much the worst for clearing off this lingering disease upon the whole nothing particular today. The admissions are five. Died 3

Saturday 20
This morning is fine with a strong breeze which made it damp and unpleasant and of course not in favour of patients. What would be of infinite service would be rain and afterwards a good strong Northerly wind. The admissions today are six. All funerals 4

The Problem of the Dead

Burying the dead in the throes of an epidemic was both a heart-wrenching experience and problematic, given the need to accommodate a large number of dead and the desire to arrange interments as quickly as possible.[122] A witness at the time, Anton, describes the scene at the burying ground of North Front during the 1828 yellow fever epidemic:

> The grave – a long deep trench extended from one side of the enclosure to the centre, in which the coffins were laid one over another, so as to fill up the vacuum. Until this method was adopted, some lay uninterred until morning. … There was no military honour paid to officer or private; all funeral parades were dropped: not a soldier accompanied, the coffin; the carman was the only mourner that attended it from the hospital to the grave.[123]

These solemn words stand in stark contrast to those written by another military man who was also present during the epidemic. Consider this description of interment by Colonel Bayly:

> Funeral processions were now seen passing the town to the burial-place on the neutral ground from morn to night; 70, 80, and sometimes 100 bodies were thrown into the long trenches dug for their reception, and as the camp was within 10 yards of this indiscriminate cemetery, the continued melancholy scene, instead of producing a serious effect on the minds of those who had escaped the malady, became in a short time a subject of mirth, and laughable speculation of insurance of lives for a week was entered into by several gay Lotharios.[124]

Yet the horrors of living through an epidemic did not go unnoticed, as the same author goes on to recount this disturbing scene:

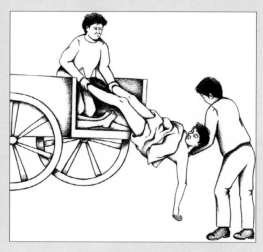

> In passing near the long trenches on the neutral ground formed for the reception of the dead, I one day observed a motion, and on a nearer approach, discovered a feeble old woman, endeavouring to drag her self from the trench. I immediately procured assistance from our pioneers and she was immediately withdrawn from the Golgotha. She had been interred the preceding evening and the earth having only par-

THE DEAD CART

Sunday 21
This a very fine morning took a walk with Alexander all round the encampment from there to Catalan Bay.[44] After sauntering and loitering about some time came back just in time for dinner and with an appetite quite sharp but Mr. W did not make his appearance till three O'clock from having taken a long walk by himself to St Michaels Cave.[45] Died 2

Monday 22
From the reports this morning am in hopes that the disease will now be taking itself without much more loss. God Almighty send it away is my sincere prayer. Have been out this afternoon to the Neutral Ground and saw Mr Heathcote Mr Lowe Mr Thompson etc, all quite well. The admissions are three. Died 1 or 4??

Tuesday 23
This by no means a pleasant morning. Dark heavy clouds with some showers but towards the middle of the day more fine. Hopes are still entertained of our getting quit of the sickness by the end of the Year. From the reports there are only one admitted. The Chronicle of yesterday mentions the following extract of a letter from New Orleans

'This town is again visited by yellow fever on its first appearance the cases were few and of similar nature, but within these few days the disease has increased and become more virulent. We have only four British vessels in port one of which the Agnes and Ann, I am sorry to say has already buried seven of her crew. All deaths 4 Died 2

tially covered her, she had contrary to all expectation, awoke from her trance just at the time of my passing by. … She…recovered and became quite a healthy woman…[125]

Clearly, the expeditious burial of yellow fever victims, while of paramount concern to health officials, was not without its problems. There was also the issue of detecting yellow fever cases early as a means of prevention. However, to prevent accidental live-burials an important precautionary regulation emerged after the experiences of the 1828 epidemic, requiring every corpse to be at least externally examined by a medical officer before any interment.[126] Though burial locations in Gibraltar were well documented, the situation in other places that passed through yellow fever epidemics is very different. Pritchett and Tunali note that "recent excavation in New Orleans uncovered the unmarked graves of at least 1600 indigent dead, some of whom may have been victims of the yellow fever epidemics of the mid-1800s."[127] Careful archaeological excavations continue to uncover these sad reminders of the power of epidemics on past populations.

WOMAN BURIED ALIVE (A. DAUST)

Wednesday 24

This is a fine morning and the appearance of the garrison is rather more lively today then it has been for some time. Suppose persons preparing for Christmas. God knows it has all the appearance of a miserable one for most of us have we have had a great many people today for ribbons and trifles. The admissions and deaths am sorry to say have increased to day. Died 3

Thursday 25

This is the coldest morning we have had in months. After breakfast went with Alexander a pretty considerable walk to St. Michaels Cave which is an immense Chasm in the Rock and appears supported by one immense pillar of putrified masses. At the far end from the mouth is a sort of figure of a woman and another representing the Sun etc etc and on the top and sides at the far end and appears beautiful work as this had been carved or had belonged to a Cathedral. The view from this is beautiful. From this cave we proceeded along the top passage of Rock to the Signal House where we met Mr Wearing, Mr Blundell, Mr Prescott they had been lunching here we came here to do the same. And proceeded along the road to St George Tower whilst there and looking through one of their Spy Glasses discovered on the high hills leading to Tariffa[46] two men and a dog now the distance from this can be little short of ten miles.

After having satisfied ourselves have we marched downwards till we came to the road leading to the Batteries on the top of the North Front which is the highest part of

Alameda, Lady Don's Garden (MFT)

the Rock. A magazine blew up here about 1816 with a tremendous explosion and has left one part of the terribly shattered burying in the ruins mortar Guns etc. The view of the encampment from this is very beautiful.

I have now the pleasant and agreeable words to write. No Fever hope to God it has ended to day. No fever.

Friday 26
This morning unexpectedly commences with rain which continues and increases as the day advances. There is nothing particular to day with the exception that there are No Cases. We are all new anxiously forward for the opening of the communication. Then for fine fun we shall be like a parcel of sailors just got on shore. All deaths 3 Died 2

Saturday 27
This is a very fine morning wonderful the difference between the mornings the following copied from the chronicle of the day

Proclamation
By his excellency Sir George Don, Knight Grand Cross of the most Honorable Military Order of the Bath, Knight Grand Cross of the Royal Quelphic Order, and of the Royal Order Cross Of Military Merit of France, General of His Majestys Forces and Colonel of the Thirty Sixth Regimental Foot, Lieutenant Governor and Commander in Chief of The Garrison and Territory of Gibraltar etc etc etc Dr Pym Chief of the Medical Department of the Garrison and Superintendent General of Quarantine in England

Dr. Alexander Broadfoot

Alexander Broadfoot[128] graduated in Edinburgh in 1803, and joined the army where he served in the Peninsular War.[129] He was Inspector General of Hospitals in the Ionian Islands in 1822, and became Deputy Inspector of Hospitals in Gibraltar in 1826 under John Hennen. After Hennen's death from yellow fever, he became Principal Medical Officer -- a very unpopular choice -- according to this Diary. To his chagrin, and to the diarist's delight, he was replaced by William Pym. Broadfoot's views on the origin of the 1828 epidemic can be summarized as follows:"From every thing in my power to learn on the subject by the Board I cannot believe that the late Epidemic [the yellow fever] originated here, but on the contrary, I think it was imported ..."[130]

Fever Strikes the Village of Catalan Bay

Yellow fever did not appear in the little village of Catalan Bay before the 21st of September, more than a month after it had broken out within the Garrison. The Commissioners 'noted that due to the isolation of Catalan Bay from the Town, it was less likely to be attacked by the epidemic'. The village is more than a mile from Town and can only be approached by a single narrow path between the North Eastern base of the Rock and the Mediterranean Sea. The first reported cases consisted of a Water Carrier and his family. This man was in the habit of carrying water on his Donkey into Town, and on return bringing back clothes to be washed by his Wife, who was a washer-woman. The second person taken ill was the servant of Captain Jenkins. The first soldier stationed at Catalan Bay to be infected with the fever was Daniel McCurry of the 12th Regiment who had assisted the Water Carrier a few days before his death to unload a bundle of clothes from his Donkey. Further cases were few in number and it was estimated that less than one-tenth of the inhabitants were attacked by the fever. At the time there were approximately 80 houses in Catalan Bay.

being of opinion that the Epidemic Fever in the Garrison has now nearly if not altogether, ceased, and it being necessary that the most decisive measures should be taken in order most effectively to destroy any remains of contagion, it is hereby ordered that all classes of Inhabitants do forthwith thoroughly cleanse and purify the interior of their several Dwellings, together with their Bedding, Clothes, and Furniture. The Inspectors of the several Districts are earnestly requested to continue their valuable exertions in the furtherance of this object, and to see, that the above measure, so important to the Public Health, be carried into complete effect. In the course of the ensuing week a board of Medical Officers accompanied by Police Sergeants, will visit the several districts for the purpose of examining such Houses and Buildings as they may deem necessary, in order that the complete purification of every part of the Town and South may be insured. And it is hereby further notified that all Bedding, Clothes, or Furniture which may be found not properly cleansed and purified, as above directed, will forthwith be destroyed.

George Don
General and Lieutenant Governor
Gibraltar 27 Dec 1828

Sunday 28
This morning after breakfast proceeded with Mr. W to take a view of the Mediterranean Steps. From our house we went through the Alamada and going up the Steps. At the top saw H. M. Orestes come to anchor and furl her sails. She was four hours from Tangier for medicine etc etc. We then proceeded along the high road round the

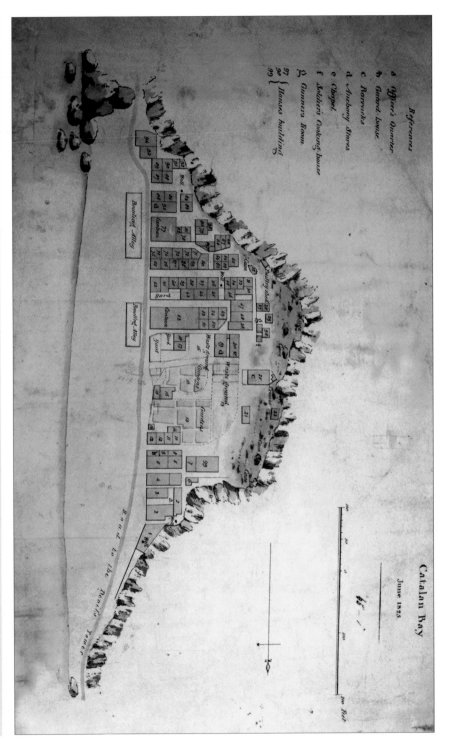

MAP OF CATALAN BAY, JUNE 1825 (PRO)

her sails. She was four hours from Tangier for medicine etc etc. We then proceeded along the high road round the end of the Jews burying ground and ascended rather a steep one till we came near a magazine very large. The road from this passes through two immense Chasms (made through the solid rock by blasting) and then continues off to the Mediterranean. All the way till you come to what becomes the Mediterranean Battery. Which is a small one mounting only two pieces looking into Catalan Bay we have rested awhile. We now began to ascend the Steps which are something in a winding form. As near as we could count from the fragments of rock and stone having broken some and filled up the places of others their numbers were 300. but are said to have been as many as first as many as the days in the Year. We halted a little while on the Top and proceeded by a rough road to St. Georges Tower which is a high round tower built apparently very strong but now is much shattered from its having been struck several times by lightning. In fact there hardly ever happens any how but this tower is struck by it. Some of the stones how lying beside it are immense. This work is however partially by the name of O'Harra's folly for when he was Governor of this Fortress he built this house and Tower for the Signal House and after he had so done government would not pay for it. So that he was obliged to pay it himself return home through the Queens Gate etc etc.[47]

PS In the Rock near Queens Gate is a very large Motar which is found in the solid Rock and is said to have been fired several times by means of a train and is loaded with large stones etc etc.

Love and Loss in the Time of Epidemics

It is difficult to capture in words the depth and scope of human tragedy that befalls individuals, families, friends, and loved ones during an epidemic. Here is one story of devotion and heartbreak that occurred in the time of yellow fever.

EUROPA POINT

Chapter Two Endnotes

[1]Martin was the chief clerk in the Civil Secretary's Office.

[2]The responsibility of the health of the Town of Gibraltar was in the hands of Gibraltar's Board of Health.

[3]The church of St. Mary the Crowned was the only Roman Catholic church in Gibraltar at the time. It was built by the Spaniards soon after they captured Gibraltar in 1462, on the site of the Moorish mosque. The church still stands in Main Street, and is now the Roman Catholic Cathedral.

[4]District 24 was one of 28 administrative districts in the town area which was thus divided to ensure a more careful surveillance of the populous town. Two civilians were appointed annually to see that a proper attention to cleanliness was observed, that houses were not overcrowded, to give early notice of such cases of sickness as came to their notice, and generally to point out any measures that would promote and secure health. A military Medical Officer was attached to four or more districts. A police sergeant had about the same number of districts.

[5]Reliable information concerning the outbreak of yellow fever cases was not universally available to the public. For example, Lieutenant Governor Don wrote to Sir George Murray (Secretary of the State) on the 4th, reporting the outbreak of the epidemic fever in the garrison.

[6]Anton (1998:89) reports that the wealthy hired accommodations on board of vessels in the bay.

[7]Sanitary cordons describes a land barrier where only those with clean bills of health can pass, were set up.

[8]The Poca Roca cave was located close to the Neutral Ground.

[9]Since the epidemic of 1813, a village had been es8tablished on the Neutral Ground, where some of the inhabitants would take up temporary residence during the warm season. This village was expanded and reorganised by the Lieutenant Governor, Sir George Don, after 1814. At the start of the yellow fever epidemic of 1828, a further encampment of tents was provided on the North Front, initially to accommodate the residents of District 24, where the fever first appeared.

[10]C091/104 Don Murray (Secretary o State) 8th September 1828- "about a thousand persons of the civil population may have been computed to have quitted the garrison before the communication with Spain was closed by the Spanish authorities, and I caused all the crowed part of the town to be evacuated by the poorer classes, about 2000 of whom are encamped on Neutral Ground, in tents which I have directed to be supplied to them."

Our diarist tells us that on the 21st of October the death of a young English officer, Mr. Cochrane, from the fever, precipitated the suicide of a young woman. Additional details of this heart-wrenching episode comes from Colonel Bayly,

> I will now relate one instance of female devotion during this horrid desolating epidemic. A beautiful young Spanish lady became deeply enamoured of one of the English officers, and was heard frequently to declare that she would not survive him if he died. He was at length attacked by the contagion, being attended to her to his expiring moments,. His body was conveyed to the usual cemetery for the officers. During this interval she had climbed a high part of the Rock, and, on the first volley of firearms denoting the interment of her lover, she precipitated herself headlong from the dizzy height and was literally dashed to atoms. She was found near Catalan Bay, with almost every bone fractured, the leg and thigh bones protruding shockingly from the flesh in pointed splinters.[131]

Like a huge tidal wave, the epidemic left fragmented remains of a society in its wake. Epidemics spare no one, even those who survived the disease. All too often those who passed through the epidemic were so grief-stricken they could not carry on with their daily lives. As the case above illustrates, a count of fever deaths alone does little justice to the devastating power of an epidemic (see Figure 7).

[11]Despite the existence of a proper Civil Hospital it is clear from this passage that there remained considerable fear and anxiety concerning the lack of adequate medical treatment available for the public.

[12]This was the name given in many British sources to the village at the head of the Bay of Gibraltar, on the road to San Roque. It is now known as Campamento.

[13]As the sickness and deaths began to accumulate there were appeals for donations. One such call was published in the local newspaper, (The Gibraltar Chronicle) on September 16th (No.2245), asking for aid for the helpless families then encamped on the Neutral Ground. The appeal was published.

[14]Lieutenant Bull of the Royal Engineers.

[15]This one of many burial grounds used in Gibraltar.

[16]On this day the Spanish Board of Health at Algeciras cut off all communication with the fortress and Town of Gibraltar, 'on pain of death'. Gibraltar Chronicle Friday September19th, 1828. No.2248

[17]Dr. Foote and Dr. Thurston were civilian medical practitioners, most of the others had Spanish qualifications.

[18]One family mentioned several times by the diarist is that of Cresswell or Creswell. Edmund Cresswell, senior emigrated from his family home in Lewes, Sussex, to Gibraltar in 1822, with his wife, four sons, and three daughters. He had been appointed "Packet Agent", in charge of the maritime mail to and from Gibraltar. Both Edmund and his wife caught the yellow fever in 1828, but recovered. Two daughters were not so lucky. Elizabeth "a very nice girl", and "the beautiful Miss Mary Creswell" both died. When Edmund died in 1831, his son, also called Edmund (born ca. 1813), took over the Packet Agency, which in 1856 was absorbed into the new Gibraltar Post Office, with Creswell as Postmaster. He was also Editor of the Gibraltar Chronicle from 1862 to 1870. When Edmund Junior died in 1877, his daughter, Margaret Creswell, was named Postmistress – the first woman to head a Government Department. She retired in 1907, putting an end to 85 years of control of the Gibraltar postal service by one family. A brother, William Rooke Creswell, joined the Royal Navy, then left for Australia and became the virtual founder of the Australian Navy.

[19]Handkerchiefs (and other objects that were porous) were seen as an agent of potential infection and was put on the list of articles to be held in quarantine during the course of an epidemic.

[20]William Oxberry's father was a prominent merchant in Gibraltar.

[21]Dr Matthias was a local doctor.

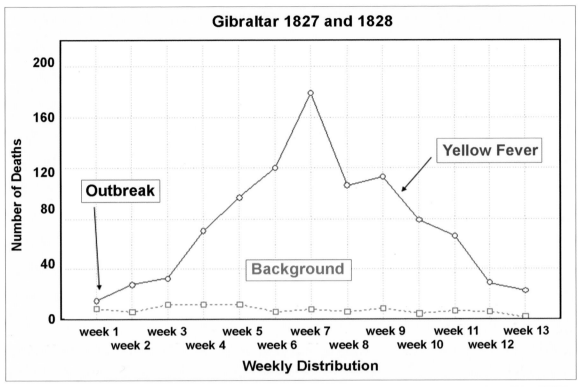

FIGURE 7. WEEKLY DEATHS

[22]Proclamation: October 6th 1828: Whereas a disease highly dangerous to the public health exists in this Fortress, and it is expedient that every endeavour should be used to prevent its clandestine introduction into the neighbouring countries. It is ordered that no vessel, or craft, under Forty Tons burthen, be permitted to clear out at, or to depart from this Port without special Permission for that purpose from his Excellency the Lieutenant Governor, on the application of the Captain of the Port. Head Quarters, By His Excellency Sir George Don

[23]To the south of the main Rock, the peninsula of Gibraltar flattens out into two main plateaus. The upper is known as Windmill Hill, and the lower as Europa Flats. Troops were quartered here during the epidemic, and were protected from infection, as the prevailing winds provided an unfavourable environment for the yellow fever mosquito.

[24]Notice: October 9th 1828 In consequence of an attempt of some individual to introduce into the Spanish Territory a Silk Hankerchief enclosed in a Letter, His Excellency General Miranda has directed, that in future, only Letters and Despatches of His Excellency the Lieutenant Governor, and as are officially addressed to the Commandant, or adjunct, of the Lines shall, be admitted at the Cordon. All other letters must be sent by the Port, and only on the regular Port days. The culpable individual who has thus attempted to infringe the Health Regulations which have been concerted with His Excellency Gen. Miranda, must justly encite the indignation of every one who has witnessed the friendly aid offered to us by the Spanish Authorities in the present emergency His Excellency the Lieutenant Governor earnestly call upon everyone to denounce to the Public Officers on the Neutral Ground every person who, to their knowledge, shall be guilty of a similar attempt, against whom His Excellency is resolved to proceed with the greatest severity.

[25]The Reverend R.J. Hatchman was Chaplin of the King's Chapel, Gibraltar. It is reported that the Chaplin buried hundreds within the first month. On October 10th he spent a long day in the cemetery. On the 12th he himself was buried. A tablet to his memory was erected on the north wall of the chancel. Officers carried on the work of burying the dead until a Methodist Minister arrived. (Source Yale, Rev. R. A Story in Stone being a History of King's Chapel Gibraltar. Pg .25. When he died, the Methodist pastor, Mr Barber, took over as Chaplain. When he died too, a lieutenant took over and officiated at funerals.

[26]Dr Peter Wilson MRCS (London and Edinburgh) was Assistant Surgeon and Purveyor at the Civil Hospital. He became Assistant Surgeon and Purveyor to the Civil Hospital in 1817, a post which he filled until just after the yellow fever of 1828.

[27]The week of the 13th to the 20th October is noted as the peak number of deaths during the 1828 epidemic.

[28]The garrison chaplain, Mr Hatchman, was infected as he performed the last offices of religion over the grade of one of the soldiers. Mr Baker, a Methodist clergyman, volunteered his service, until another appointment should take place, but in three days thereafter, he also laid in the grave. REF page 90 -

[29]Covered carts, called dead wagons, were stationed at certain places, on purpose to receive the dead and carry them to the grave-yard. Anton, 91.

[30]The Chronicle first appeared in 1801, and has been published continuously for over 200 years. The only gap in its appearance was one of several months, during the yellow fever epidemic of 1804. Originally published weekly, by 1828 it was a daily newspaper published by the Garrison Library. The post of Editor of the Gibraltar Chronicle for at least the period up to 1877 was held by a Military or Civil Officer in Her Majesty's Service.

[31]Not only did the increase in physicians increase the level of available medical care in the town but it also it raised the public's perception in concern for their welfare by the colonial authorities.

[32]In the 18th and 19th centuries, Tangier was the most important source of food supplies in Morocco for Gibraltar, with the exception of Tetuan. Relations between the Governor of Gibraltar and the Sultan of Morocco were usually good, but the British Navy blockaded Tangier in November 1828, in reprisal for difficulties made by the authorities there in supplying food for Gibraltar. The blockade was lifted in January, when the crisis caused by the epidemic had passed.

[33]This was situated on Middle Hill, the central of the three peaks forming the upper ridge of the Rock. The lookout there provided early warning of ships approaching from the Mediterranean or through the Straits.

[34]This is contrary evidence to actual cause of death as published documents state that Mr Nahon died on 2nd November with bloodshot eyes and vomit which was not black, which was attributed to the medicines which he had been given. In fact, Dr Foote declared in writing that he had died of apoplexy. Documens relatifs a l'épidemie de fièvre jaune qui a regné a Gibraltar en 1828 Vol II, p132:By Chervin, Louis, Trousseau and Barry. Paris 1830

[35]Deals are a type of wood.

[36]In the time of an epidemic, social activities and amusements would all have been curtailed leaving the inhabitants with little to do but deal with issues of the epidemic.

[37]Subscriptions for the poor were an important means of providing aid the inhabitants as Gibraltar did not have any Poor Laws or a state run form of welfare. It is also noteworthy that there were strong links with England and Scotland.

[38]Dr Dicks (Dix) was an army surgeon. He was Acting Surgeon of the Civil Hospital from 1830-1832.

[39]Lieutenant Forsteen of the 12th Foot Regiment.

[40]Lieutenant-Colonel Payne of the Royal Artillery.

[41]Care giving during the course of yellow fever should not be underestimated.

[42]In 1815, the area around the grand parade was laid out with gardens and walks by General Sir George Don. The project was financed by the proceeds of several lotteries. It became known as the Alameda (Thornton spells it "Alamada"). The area had previously been a barren slope of red sand, used as a burial ground. It was, and still remains, Gibraltar's only significant area of parkland.

[43]It was five years earlier when the first vessel (Steam packet Royal George) propelled by steam arrived at Gibraltar on 10th October, 1823.

[44]A month had elapsed since the first appearance of yellow fever in Catalan Bay and presumably at this time it was free of the epidemic. The first reported cases [on the 21st of September] consisted of a Water Carrier and his family. This man was in the habit of carrying water on his Donkey into Gibraltar, and on return bringing back clothes to be washed by his Wife, who was a washer-woman. Further cases were few in number and it was estimated that less than one-tenth of the inhabitants were attacked by the fever.

[45]St Michael's Cave has always been a well-known attraction of the Rock, and was traditionally thought to be bottomless. It has remarkable stalactite and stalagmite formations, and is part of an extensive system of caves, which includes a large fresh water lake.

[46]The most southerly town in Spain. It was defended against the Moors by Guzman el Bueno, who later captured Gibraltar (1309). During the Peninsular War it was successfully defended by the British against an assault by the French.

[47]Lieutenant General Charles O'Hara, who was Governor of Gibraltar from 1795 until his death in 1802, built this tower at the southern end of the ridge near the highest point of the Rock. It is said that he believed that from this vantage point, he would be able to look over the hills of Spain into Cadiz harbour and spy on the Spanish fleet's movements. For obvious reasons, it soon became known as O'Hara's Folly.

Notes Endnotes

[48]It is important to acknowledge that any account of an epidemic at the time of the crisis is seldom free of bias or self interest. While Thornton's diary forms a cornerstone of this work, it is only one voice and accordingly, it does not reflect the collective experience of the populace. For example, most of Thornton's personal references to the sick and dying refer to the Protestant civilians or military.

[49]Historical Sketch of the Epidemic Yellow Fever which prevailed at Gibraltar in the Autumn of 1828. Lancet 1829/30. p. 325-330.

[50]Conceptually, medical topographies are geographical rather than medical studies, because their organizing principle is spatial rather than medical.

[51]Barrett, 2000, 191-193.

[52]Wilson, 30-32.

[53]Wilson, 44-45.

[54]General Don to Lord Bathurst, 29th October 1814.

[55]Twelve members of the family went through the fever - four were bedridden, of which one died.

[56]Wilson 1830, 135-141.

[57]The regulations called for any ship carrying these articles arriving from an infected location to immediately quit the port, roadstead or anchorage ground of Gibraltar.

[58]A comprehensive description of the measures taken can be found in Bland 1752.

[59]Barry 1830, 4.

[60]Not unexpectedly, strangers or outsiders served as convenient scapegoats to explain the origins of disease. These groups were shunned, isolated, expelled and demonised. European communities often blamed the presence of Jews or Gypsies, and those in British cities during the cholera epidemics blamed the Irish. See, for example, Coles 1986; McNeill 1976.

[61]Ngalamulume 2004, 194.

[62]Ngalamulume 2004, 195.

[63]SAWCHUK - CHOLERA

[64]Although the regulations remained in place on the books, it is questionable that true isolation remained intact as individuals could undermine regulations through smuggling and disobedience. Moreover, it was typically the poorly paid civil servants responsible for the maintenance of quarantine who could be corrupted.

[65] GGA Miscellaneous Letters. Governor C. Campbell to General Hadia of Algeciras. 10 October 1810.

[66] From correspondence to the Governor, we learn that M. Morgan, the Director of the Police has requested additional funds of 2 dollars per day as the result of his extra duties and fatigue as he is required to sit on horseback for nearly 5 hours in heat and strong sun.

[67] Louis 1839; Amiel 1829.

[68] CO 91/53. Response to questions Re: yellow fever 1813/14. Jo. D. Gilpin M.D. D. Inspect. of Hospitals.

[69] Kopperman 2004, 539.

[70] Kopperman 2004, 543.

[71] Kopperman 2004.

[72] See Sawchuk and Burke 1998.

[73] Howard-Jones 1972, 373.

[74] Worth Estes and Smith 1997, 8.

[75] Amiel, 1828.

[76] CO 91/58. Extract of a letter from Mr. John Gardiner, Surgeon of the Naval Hospital at Gibraltar addressed to the Commissioners for Transport, October 30, 1813.

[77] CO 91/103. Report by Dr. Pym on the number who had passed through the fever in the Garrison, 1829.

[78] Records indicate that during the yellow fever outbreak there were 54 District Inspectors in the Town and 16 located in the South.

[79] Pym 1828? ... on Yellow Fever. p.34.

[80] Gibraltar Chronicle January 12th 1829. No. 2346

[81] Information on the nature of yellow fever during the preceding epidemics was variable; for example, during the 1804 epidemic the newspaper ceased publication completely, while during the 1813 epidemic, only statistical tables were given with no commentary whatsoever.

[82] No. 2243 Gibraltar Chronicle Saturday 13th 1828. This appeal also appeared at an earlier date on Wednesday, September 10th 1828, No. 2240.

[83] Gibraltar Chronicle Friday September, 12th 1828. No. 2242

[84] Gibraltar Chronicle Saturday, 13th 1828. No. 2243

[85] Gibraltar Chronicle September 27th 1828. No. 2255.

[86] Havana, Cuba was an important source of tobacco and sugar. Unfortunately, it was also often the source of the yellow fever virus.

[87]Gibraltar Chronicle August 16th 1828. No. 2219.

[88]One such illustration is the article, "Is the Yellow Fever Contagious?", originally published in the Medical Repository which was republished in the Gibraltar Chronicle Wednesday, March 3rd 1824. No. 1832.

[89]Gibraltar Chronicle Tuesday, September 16th 1828. No. 2245.

[90]The Late Epidemic at Gibraltar, and its Victims. United Service Magazine, Volume 19, 1830, pages 102-103 (Signed T).

[91]Anonymous 1830. The Soldier's Cemetery at Gibraltar. United Service Magazine, p. 720.

[92]See Rosenburg (1962, 1966) for a review of the role of the atmosphere as the cause of cholera in 19th century America.

[93]Climate can act as a stressor, upsetting physiological homeostasis through temperature, moisture and so forth. Further, human activity patterns are affected by weather and in turn can affect the physical wellbeing of individuals. Finally, the weather can affect growth and harvesting of food which in turn, under adverse conditions, can yield dramatic nutritional and economic effects. The impact of changes in climate on mortality rates have been addressed in numerous studies. See, for example, Mather 1974; Alderson 1985.

[94]Based on meteorological returns from 1850 to 1995, the mean annual rainfall for a 'rain year' in Gibraltar was 849.7 mm.

[95]For a discussion of the relationship of climatic factors and the yellow fever epidemic of 1804, see Sawchuk and Burke 1997, 1998.

[96]William Coleman – Yellow Fever in the North.

[97]Humphreys, Margaret 1997 Yellow Fever: the Yellow Jack. In Plague, Pox and Pestilence. Edited by Kenneth F. Kiple. Phoenix Illustrated, London. P. 88.

[98]Gilbard 1883, 15.

[99]Sawchuk 1993, 879.

[100]Miège 1984.

[101]Barry 1830, 5.

[102]Garratt 1939, 110.

[103]GGA Major-General Sir Alexander Woodford. Executive No. 16, Gibraltar, January 23, 1839.

[104]CO 91/39, April 1797, O'Hara to the Duke of Portland.

[105]Ford 1855, 363-64.

[106]Augustin 1909, 561. In 1813, it was claimed that Gibraltar, in turn, served as the source of infection for the introduction of yellow fever to Málaga (Augustin 1909, 592).

[107]Pym, 1848; Dictionary of National Biography: Article on Sir William Pym

[18]In 1815 he published Observations on the Bulam Fever (his name for yellow fever), and was regarded as the definitive authority on the disease for many years, with a second edition being published in 1848.

[109]He was made Inspector of Army Hospitals in 1816 and, in 1826, he became Superintendent-General of Quarantine.

[110]The three French physicians who had also come to Gibraltar to investigate the causes of the epidemic produced a voluminous report, but no conclusions, even though one of their group, Nicholas Chervin, was a steadfast non-contagionist and non-importationist.

[111]Fraser 1822, 9.

[112]Watts 1997, 170-71.

[113]Amiel 1829, 17.

[114]Clarke 1831/32, 915.

[115]Sawchuk 2001.

[116]Jacquelyn Miller 2001.

[117]Miller 2001, 133.

[118]Miller 2001.

[119]Chalhoub 1993, 447.

[120]His sons, too, both medical students, volunteered as assistants in the Civil Hospital. One of them, John Hennen Jr, wrote a memoir of his father as a foreword to an edition of his father's "Principles of Military Surgery", published in 1830.

[121]WO 43/373 24th November 1828 to F.R. Somerset from J.M. Gregor (Director General).

[122]Covered carts, called dead wagons, were strategically stationed at certain places, to receive the dead and carry them to the graveyard (Anton 1998, 91).

[123]Anton 1998, 93.

[124]Bayly 1896, 270.

[125]Bayly 1896, 276-77.

[126]Barry 1830, 11.

[127]Pritchett and Tunali 1995, 518.

[128]See Benady 1994.

[129]He was made Inspector of Quarantine, a new post, which he kept until 1835. Benjamin Disraeli, who visited Gibraltar in 1831, speaks highly of him. He died in Chatham in 1837.

[130]CO91/102 Dr. Broadfoot 224 Gibraltar. 30 April, 1829.

[131]Bayly, 275

-3-

The Weight of an Epidemic

GIBRALTAR FROM THE NORTH WEST

A Part of Everyday Life

A review of the yellow fever outbreaks in Gibraltar demonstrates that the disease was: (1) epidemic in nature, (2) sporadic in its occurrence over time, (3) variable in its morbidity and mortality, (4) and finally, subject to eventual extinction. It is important to understand that by 1828 the idea of fever had become an integral part of life in Gibraltar. Those who survived the epidemic (and consequently became immune to the fever) saw the disease in a completely different light than a 'newcomer' or family that had not 'passed through' the fever. From a foreign perspective, the situation was seen as surreal: two distinct classes of inhabitants – the immune and the susceptible - co-existing in time and space.

A Delicate Balance

So, why did yellow fever emerge in epidemic proportions? It is important to realize that in order for yellow fever to appear, a 'delicate balance' of conditions must coalesce. Gibraltar met these conditions.[1] The most important of these conditions was that the virus had to first be introduced into the community, either through the arrival of an infected human or mosquito (see Figure 8). Gibraltar's strategic location and linkage to the global community (via trade and colonialism) greatly facilitated the importation of yellow fever. Second, ecological conditions had to be suitable for the mosquito (the carrier of the yellow fever virus) to survive, feed, and reproduce. Such conditions were easily met in Gibraltar's hot summer months, when mosquitoes were observed to "swarm in myriads, and greatly increase the apparent heat of the atmosphere, by the state of irritation in which they constantly keep the skin"[2] A third critical factor, the presence of a sufficient number of susceptible or non-immune individuals in the community.[3] By 1828, that particular condition had clearly been met through a high birth rate and a large influx of newcomers to the Rock with no prior exposure to the virus.

Meeting these primary factors, the crowded and unsanitary urban landscape of Gibraltar further assisted the development of epidemic yellow fever. Arguably, the most important of these factors was patio living, where large concentrations of potentially susceptible people lived within confined and limited space. Further, patios offered an ideal niche for mosquito breeding since courtyards were often poorly

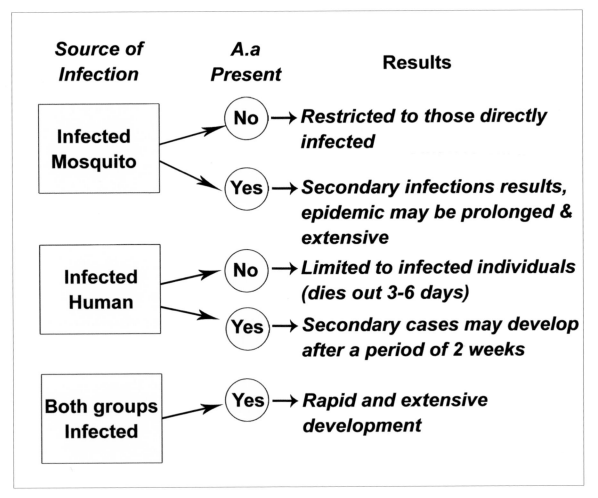

FIGURE 8. CONDITIONS NECESSARY FOR AN EPIDEMIC

paved, inadequately drained, and shut off from strong winds and direct sunlight. More so, the daily washing and drying of clothes in these shaded and unventilated courtyards produced stagnant pools of water that did not dry out even during summer droughts. Water storage containers, barrels, buckets, and earthen jugs or *tinajas* created ideal breeding grounds for the mosquito vector. Since most houses lacked glass windows or screens, mosquitoes easily made their way through the wooden shutters.

If Gibraltar's housing conditions facilitated the progress of yellow fever, local meteorological conditions were critical in marking the cessation of the epidemic. This fact was not lost on the diarist in this text and other residents of Gibraltar who recognized that the colder weather brought relief from yellow fever. The disappearance of yellow fever in the winter can now be easily explained: Aedes can only feed when the temperature is above 59° to 63° F. Graphing the reconstruction of the monthly maximum temperatures in Gibraltar from June of 1828 (shown below) there is clear evidence of why the yellow fever epidemic extinguished itself in the cold month of January, 1829 (see Figure 9).

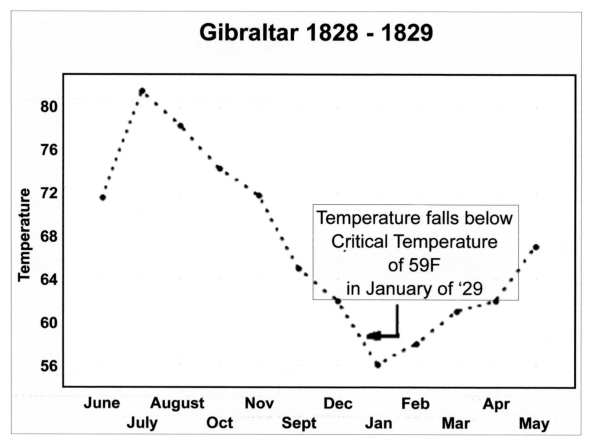

FIGURE 9. TEMPERATURE CONDITIONS NECESSARY FOR THE YELLOW FEVER EPIDEMIC

As to why epidemic yellow fever ceased to be a problem in Gibraltar after 1828, it is likely that a significant improvement in nautical technology and improved quarantine measures made the difference. According to Smith and Gibson (1986), the substitution of steam power for sail power, and the replacement of water barrels for a piped water supply represented the most critical developments:

> By the early 1850s, transatlantic shipping was rapidly changing from sail to steam. The steamships were new and had piped water supplies. [As a result], A aegypti was much less likely to establish breeding colonies on board. At the same time, they crossed the Atlantic much more rapidly - around 2 weeks as compared with 5, 6 or more weeks for sailing vessels. Ship-borne yellow fever was thus much less likely to lead to the release of infected mosquitoes on arrival in Europe, but steamships were more likely to arrive with yellow fever still active.

A revised set of quarantine measures put forth in 1830[4] in Gibraltar by the Lieutenant Governor also played a role in preventing the reoccurrence of yellow fever visitations in Gibraltar, by restricting the entry of ships from 'fever countries' during the hot summer months.[5]

Counting the Dead

While basic counts of the dead invariably understate the misery and grief associated with an epidemic,[6] they can at least provide a crude indication of the relative impact of an episode of crisis mortality on a population. By 1828, Gibraltarians had gone through three similar fever epidemics and consequently, it may be argued that this experience, and greater familiarity with the disease, may have contributed to a more organized and accurate count of the lives taken. Officially, 1,677 died of yellow fever in total. Sergeant Anton, present during the epidemic, estimates the death toll to at least 2,300; the official figure being an underestimate, in his opinion, due to a concealment of or failure to report yellow fever deaths.[7] It is also worth mentioning that Gibraltar was much more of anorganized community in 1828 under Don's guidance than it was in 1804 and that social disruption was less and hence there was a more accurate accounting of the inhabitants.

One method of estimating the reliability of the official tally is to compute the case-fatality rate, defined as the number of yellow fever deaths divided by the total number of individuals who contracted the disease. Contemporary researchers report case-fatality rates ranging from 15 to 50 percent or higher; very high rates suggest mild cases going unrecognized or not reported as yellow fever.[8] Table 7 shows that 5,681 civilians passed through the fever in 1828. With 1,170 civilian deaths due to yellow fever, we can estimate the Gibraltar yellow fever case-fatality rate at 20% (or 20 deaths per 100 cases), therefore, we can argue that at this time there was little under-reporting of yellow fever deaths in Gibraltar by 1828.

The Issue of Susceptibility

If it is difficult to arrive at accurate mortality statistics during an epidemic, it is very difficult to gauge whether or not everyone was equally vulnerable to attack by the yellow fever virus.[9] One contemporary scholar summed up perceptions regarding susceptibility in this way:

> Yellow fever was believed to prefer victims of mature years, with children and old people relatively, but not exclusively, exempt. The greater number of cases seemed to occur in persons between fourteen and forty, and strangely, the healthy and well-nourished appeared most likely to die. Slender, "nervous" individuals frequently escaped altogether or recovered quickly. Women seemed less susceptible than men, and they also had more favourable prospects of survival. Race and "acclimation", however, were considered to be the most decisive of all factors.[10]

How the Gibraltar experience with yellow fever compared with these observations warrants consideration now.

Location	Year	Men	Women	Children	Total
Persons who have Passed Through the Fever					
Garrison	1804	1215	1174		2,389
	1813	1154	1066		2,220
	1814	150	141		291
	1828	1121	1089	3078	5,288
Catalan Bay and Neutral Ground	1804	287	283		570
	1813	287	235		522
	1814	38	38		76
	1828	102	75	216	393
					11,749
Persons who have Not Passed Through the Fever					
Garrison	1828	170	119	625	914
Catalan Bay and Neutral Ground	1828	592	662	1553	2,807

TABLE 7. RETURN OF THE NUMBER OF PERSONS WHO HAVE AND HAVE NOT PASSED THROUGH THE EPIDEMIC FEVER[11]

As to treatment, an extant record of the patient register for the Civil Hospital[12] (reproduced in part in Table 8) gives the reader the opportunity to gain deeper insight into aspects of yellow fever morbidity (i.e. sickness) and mortality in Gibraltar. With 167 deaths in the Civil Hospital, and 1,170 civilian deaths overall, it appears that the majority of yellow fever deaths occurred at home. Those who entered the hospital were disproportionately male.[13] Most patients were sick with the fever for at least two days before entering the hospital. For those who recovered, most had first endured 8 days of sickness.[14]

The calculation of case fatality rates (CFR) from the hospital records is equally enlightening. The overall CFR of 20 per 100 cases, computed earlier for the entire civilian community, stands in marked contrast to 36 per 100 cases computed for the Civil Hospital patients. One possible explanation – individuals sent to the hospital had more

Names	Age	Nation	N of days ill previous to admission	Admit	Dis-charge	Died	Duration of Illness
Juan Cafire	11	Spaniard	3	21A	24A		5
Mary Silcox	34	English	7	29A			11
Guillermo Suary	40	Spaniard	4	30A		1S	8
Mary Flynn	30	English		1S	8S	2S	8
John Suary	16	Spaniard	4	1S			10
Pedro Androbib	50	"	3	2S	19S	6S	21
Jose Peres	12	"	1	2S	12S		12
Antonio Restano	10	"	1	2S			7
Moses Bocasis	44	Hebrew	3	3S		7S	6
Samuel Benhaim	50	"	1	3S	7S	5S	6
Eleyau Benhaim	11	"	1	3S	7S		6
Francisco Traino	28	Spaniard	1	3S			6
David Benarus	25	Hebrew	1	3S	4S	7S	2
John Podsal	56	English	5	4S			6
James Heys	44	"	4	5S		5S	5
Meshod Benhaim	14	Hebrew	1	5S	11S	6S	8
Abram Benhaim	6	"	1	5S	11S		8
Edward Acres	22	English	1	5S	15S		12
Pedro Ricando	51	Spaniard	1	5S			5
Pedro Ricando	51	"	2	5S		7S	4
Catalina de Ode	8	"	1	6S	7S	8S	3
Elen Gilmore	26	English	1	6S			7
Ana Suari	18	Spaniard	2	6S	7S	10S	3
Juan Alcaldi	7	"	1	6S	21S		15
Pedro Alcaldi	5	"	1	6S			5
Juance Picherichi	14	Genoese	1	6S	14S	9S	12
Maria Hoare	35	English	3	6S			7
Antonio Garcia	51	Spaniard	1	6S	14S	11S	12
Victori Lopez	50	"	3	6S	18S		15
Latitia Fallen	30	English	3	6S	11S		5

TABLE 8. GENERAL RETURN OF PATIENTS AFFECTED WITH THE EPIDEMIC FEVER, ADMITTED, DISCHARGED AND DIED AT THE CIVIL HOSPITAL DURIND THE YEAR 1828.[15]

severe cases of yellow fever. The suggestion that the young were less likely to die of yellow fever is borne out by the findings reported in Table 9, which shows a clear age gradient. Another interesting discovery is that while there were inter-group differentials in CFRs according to natality (see Table 10), the disparity was not statistically significant.

Age	N of Deaths	Total Patients	Case Fatality Rate
Under 20	*34*	*135*	*251.9*
20-29	*50*	*137*	*365.0*
30-39	*37*	*91*	*406.6*
40-49	*30*	*67*	*447.8*
50 plus	*16*	*34*	*470.6*

TABLE 9. HOSPITAL CASE FATALITY RATES BY AGE.

Group	N of Deaths	Total Patients	Case Fatality Rate
Hebrew	*17*	*43*	*395.3*
English	*39*	*120*	*325.0*
Foreigners	*111*	*301*	*368.8*

TABLE 10. HOSPITAL CASE FATALITY RATES BY NATION

As to the claim that females were less susceptible to the yellow fever virus than males,[16] we turn to an examination of the Roman Catholic parish death records for the period between 1826 and 1829. The results for Gibraltar presented in Table 11 suggest that despite there being a nearly equal number of adult males and females in the population,[17] there was a significantly higher death rate among males. This disparity in mortality by sex increased substantially during the yellow fever epidemic.[18] Besides the possibility of physiologically-based explanations for the difference, there may be a number of gender-based explanations for these results. One possibility is that males held occupations that put them at greater risk of coming into contact with infected individuals or the mosquito vector. Another factor may be that migrant males were more likely to be without kin or friends in Gibraltar and, as such, they were less likely to receive care in their time of sickness.

Gibraltar: 1826 - 1833			
	Male	Female	M/F Ratio
Epidemic Year - 1828			
Sept to Dec	40.1	15.5	2.66
Jan to Aug	2.1	1.3	1.60
Non-Epidemic Years			
Jan to Dec	2.1	1.2	1.75

TABLE 11. MONTHLY DEATH RATES DURING THE PERIOD 1826 TO 1833 AMONG ROMAN CATHOLICS.[19]

Finally, given the fact that Gibraltar is a colony, there is the opportunity to critically evaluate whether the military (colonizer) fared any better than the civilians (colonized) during an epidemic (see Figure 10 and 11). In Gibraltar, we know that the military and civilians occupied different social positions but generally endured, over the long-term, the same environmental conditions; both groups shared a common exposure to the same pathogens, the same sanitary defects, and the same squalid urban conditions. On the other hand, based on our earlier findings, one would expect the military, with their predominantly male composition and a disease-favourable age distribution, to show higher yellow fever mortality rates.

Figure 10 provides a graphic comparison of the number of deaths in the two communities, while Figure 11 shows the corresponding yellow fever mortality rates. The latter graph clearly highlights the benefits experienced by the civilian community by virtue of previous exposure to fever epidemics. Such an advantage was also observed by colonial officials; Lieutenant-Governor Don noted, at that time, that the garrison was "comprised of young soldiers, few or any of whom had been seasoned in warm climates, thus providing ample food for the ravages of the disease."[20] One manifestation of this difference in herd immunity can be seen in the disparity in overall yellow fever mortality rates between the two groups – 101.4 deaths per 1000 living among the military, and 75.6 deaths per 1000 living among the civilians. It would appear that the colonizers, with little previous experience with the disease, fared much worse than the colonized.

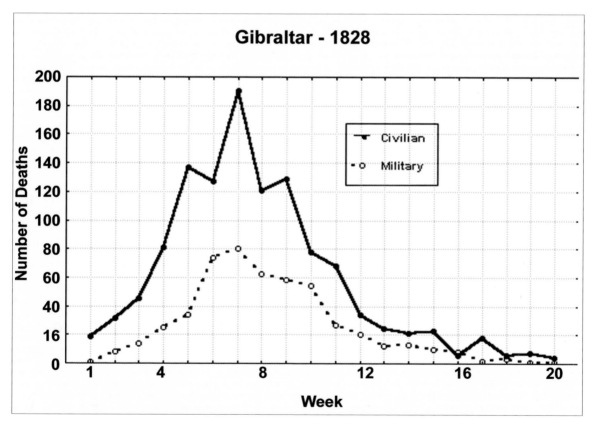

FIGURE 10. WEEKLY NUMBER OF YELLOW FEVER DEATHS

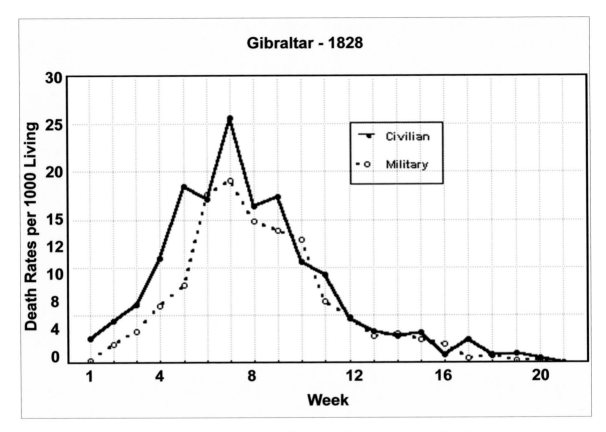

FIGURE 11. YELLOW FEVER DEATH RATES PER 1000 LIVING

Before drawing any final conclusions regarding the impact of yellow fever on these groups, there is the issue of addressing the number of individuals at risk. Under the simplest of situations, the 'population at risk' (of dying) is equal to the number of people present in the population, in this case provided by the census count of 15,470. However, we know that some inhabitants were said to have escaped Gibraltar shortly after the news of the outbreak. Assuming that the population that managed to make it out was about 1,000, the population at risk is better estimated at 14,470. Another important revision comes from our knowledge that those who passed through the fever were not susceptible to subsequent attacks and, therefore, are not fairly included in the estimates of the population at risk of dying (since, among those previously infected and surviving, there is no risk in subsequent epidemics). Information gathered by Dr. Pym after the 1828 epidemic indicates that 6,068 of the resident civilian population had passed through the 1804, 1813, and 1814 epidemics; as a result, the population at risk is better estimated at 7,402. Based on this revised denominator, the yellow fever mortality rate among civilians is closer to 158.06 per 1,000 – nearly double our original estimate. Under this scenario, the civilian community suffered modestly higher rates relative to the military during the 1828 epidemic. Figure 10 shows that this disparity was most heavily exerted in the first 8 weeks of the outbreak (see also Tables 12 and 13).

One might suggest that the military benefited from better medical care and greater isolation from areas of infestation through the rapid and selective removal of personnel to the 'safe areas'.[21] While both civilians and military were ordered to safe areas, the civilians were more likely to try and to succeed in evading the move. There is additional evidence that, relative to the military, civilians were more likely to face the problem of obtaining a sufficient supply of clean, wholesome, and potable water,

> Water is not plentiful in the summer months, it is not attainable by the poorer classes with purchase and that after with difficulty. The water made use of by the Poor is generally brackish water from the Neutral Ground and the water even from the wells of the Garrison is not pure and often thick and muddy.[22]

Another early account gives further support that the military population was better supplied since civilian water was "...so bad, and the scarcity...so great, that [the civilians] sometimes pay five reals (near two shillings sterling) for a small keg of better water, which they buy from the soldiers".[23] According to military practice, the amount of potable water available to soldiers and their families was rationed according to rank, age, and sex.[24] Commanding officers received seven gallons of water per day; non-commissioned officers and the rank and file were allotted two-and-a-half gallons per day. Military wives were also rationed two-and-a-half gallons per day, and their children received one gallon a day.[25] The importance of obtaining a sufficient quantity of drinking water during the epidemic should not be underestimated, as rehydration is imperative if the disease is to be withstood, particularly for those with milder cases of yellow fever who are more likely to overcome the virus if provided with supportive care.

Period		Inhabitants			
From	*To*	*Men*	*Women*	*Children*	*Total*
1	*7*	*10*	*4*	*5*	*19*
Sept					
8	*14*	*13*	*9*	*10*	*32*
15	*21*	*30*	*8*	*7*	*45*
22	*28*	*51*	*21*	*9*	*81*
29	*5*	*82*	*35*	*20*	*137*
	Oct				
6	*12*	*85*	*21*	*29*	*127*
13	*19*	*45*	*43*	*32*	*190*
20	*26*	*78*	*26*	*17*	*121*
27	*2 Nov*	*77*	*33*	*19*	*129*
3	*9*	*50*	*19*	*9*	*78*
10	*16*	*31*	*26*	*11*	*68*
17	*23*	*13*	*11*	*10*	*34*
24	*30*	*10*	*10*	*4*	*24*
1 Dec	*7*	*9*	*3*	*9*	*21*
8	*14*	*11*	*6*	*6*	*23*
15	*21*	*3*	*1*	*2*	*6*
22	*28*	*8*	*8*	*2*	*18*
29	*4*	*4*	*1*	*1*	*6*
	Jan				
	1829				
5	*11*	*2*		*5*	*7*
12	*14*	*2*	*1*	*1*	*4*
Total		*684*	*286*	*200*	*1170*

TABLE 12. YELLOW FEVER DEATHS
AMONG THE CIVILIAN INHABITANTS
DURING THE 1828 EPIDEMIC.[26]

Period		Military				
From	To	Officers	Men	Women	Children	Total
1 Sept	7		1			1
8	15		6		2	8
15	21	1	11	1	1	14
22	28	1	22		2	25
29	5 Oct		31	2	1	34
6	12	1	67	3	3	74
13	19		75	3	2	80
20	26		56	4	2	62
27	2 Nov		53	3	2	58
3	9	1	51		2	54
10	16	2	23	1	1	27
17	23	1	19			20
24	30	1	6		5	12
1 Dec	7	1	9		3	13
8	14		7		3	10
15	21		7	1		8
22	28		2		2	2
29	4 Jan 1829				3	3
5	11		1			1
12	14		1			1
Total		9	448	18	32	507

TABLE 13. YELLOW FEVER DEATHS AMONG THE MILITARY COMMUNITY DURING THE 1828 EPIDEMIC[27]

Gauging The Weight of An Epidemic: Other Examples

As just illustrated, it is very difficult to accurately gauge the impact of any epidemic beyond the immediate death toll. It is important to recognize that the computation of yellow fever mortality rates from historical records is not an easy task. The case of Gibraltar is no exception, as research in other populations has yielded similar difficulties.

A common goal for researchers interested in evaluating the impact of epidemics on populations is the estimation of mortality risks, or literally how many people perished in an epidemic. Standardized measures include cause-specific mortality or life expectancy in times of crisis. Generally, two types of information are needed to calculate mortality risks: the number of persons dying from the cause of death under study, and the population size (or, the number of persons available to die in the population). The further back in history the researcher goes, particularly before governments took an active role in collecting information about their citizens, the harder it is to produce accurate estimates. Researchers have to be opportunistic, locating good quality sources which are often buried deep in archives and libraries. For excellent examples of this research process and the types of materials that can be found, see Herring and Swedlund's *Human Biologists in the Archives*.[28]

As a case in point, in their study of the impact of the 1853 yellow fever epidemic in New Orleans, Pritchett and Tunali use two different sources of information in two different publications: 1) the records of interments maintained by sextons during the epidemic[29] and, 2) the admission book of Charity Hospital in New Orleans for the year 1853.[30]

In the first study listed here, using the sextons' records, Pritchett and Tunali encountered two significant issues. The first had to do with their ability to accurately estimate the number of people at risk of dying from yellow fever during the 1853 epidemic. New Orleans saw a significant outpouring of individuals fleeing the city, terrified of the yellow fever outbreak. As a result, the deaths that they capture in their study can really only reflect the portion of the population that stayed in the city, which is a hard number to estimate. That being said, there were further problems in calculating an accurate number of deaths owing to "the possibility that some yellow fever deaths were not recorded"[31] since the government did not enforce any mandatory death registration (prior to 1914 in Louisiana). In addition, "newspaper editors complained that the overworked sextons did not report all of their interments and that 'some parties pulls up the pickets of the fence and bury their dead without certificate or any account being taken".[32] To add to the problem of estimating the dead, sextons were not terribly rigorous with the information they collected in the interment records, and the sex of the dead was notably absent. As a result, the researchers attempted to infer sex where possible based on the name of the deceased.

The Charity Hospital record book is a rare and valuable resource, providing a host of information for each admission record: date of admission, date of death or discharge, first and last name, race, occupation, place of birth, age, length of residence in New Orleans, location of residence prior to arrival in New Orleans (for migrants), marital status, length of illness as of the time of admission, and a brief description of the malady.[33] Tunali and Pritchett note that the records were handwritten by different individuals and that microfilms of the original admission book had to be read and entered into a database program in the library. The authors recognize a significant advantage to these records is grounded in the fact that all information was gathered from the patient (as opposed to a third party) at the time of admission, which would likely reduce the number of reporting errors.

Using the sextons' records, and allowing for caveats, Pritchett and Tunali estimate a yellow fever mortality rate (number of deaths from yellow fever divided by the population at risk of dying, standardized per 1000 in the population) for the population of New Orleans as a whole at 52/1000; among all foreign born at 125/1000 and among all U.S. born at 9/1000 during the 1853 epidemic.[34] Comparing these estimates, it is clear that the label 'stranger's disease' holds true in this study, with the foreign born segment of the population at far greater risk of dying from yellow fever than those born within the United States. Because of emigration during the epidemic, however, and only periodic population censuses, it was difficult to calculate a precise mortality rate. As a result, Pritchett and Tunali also calculate a 'proportional mortality ratio' which simply measures the proportion of all deaths within a group that are attributable to a particular health risk (in this case, yellow fever). As with the first analysis, they calculated proportional mortality ratios that were consistently higher for the foreign born population, but note no major difference between the various foreign-born groups in terms of yellow fever morality risks. As a result, Pritchett and Tunali find good quantitative support for the notion of yellow fever broadly being a 'stranger's disease', as opposed to an 'Irish', 'French', or 'German' disease – all those who were foreign-born shared an evident weakness (due to lack of previous exposure) to yellow fever in the Western Hemisphere.

In his examination of the impact of the 1849-1850 yellow fever epidemic in Rio de Janeiro, Brazil, Chalhoub relies on the death estimations published by José Pereira Rego in 1851.[35] Rego's calculations include both the number of individuals who contracted the disease, and the number of people who died from the disease. According to Chalhoub, Rego reportedly collected these numbers from compilations of hospital records and other sources; the quality of Rego's publication is rare, in the sense that he was "the only one who bothered to indicate from where he was drawing his numbers."[36] Rego's estimates were later reported by the government as the official estimates of sickness and death attributable to the epidemic. Interestingly, Chalhoub points out that "during the outbreak…the imperial government forbade newspapers to publish the daily number of victims, and did its best to conceal the real extent of the epidemic."[37] In an attempt to prevent mass chaos and fear among the local population and not wanting to scare off economic activities, concealment of the magnitude of the sick and dead was common practice, though, as Chalhoub notes, "it obviously led to much confusion and wild speculation as to the real number of vict-ims."[38] As a result, researchers must always be critical of the accuracy of published accounts. In England, Smith and Gibson note that newspaper accounts of a small yellow fever epidemic, which appeared in South Wales in 1865,[39] did not accurately reflect the details supplied from official documents such as crew lists and a detailed report compiled by a medical inspector charged with the task.[40]

As a general note, various political or organizational agendas could also influence what was deemed important to record, greatly influencing what appears in archives today. In Löwy's work, she noted that a scientific agenda left little room for studying the social, cultural, and economic context of yellow fever. In a critical examination of the documents produced through the activities of the Rockefeller Foundation (a philanthropic American public health agency) in Brazil in the early 20th century, Löwy notes "the RF experts attempted in their letters, diaries, reports, scientific papers, and 'discovery accounts' to impose order and structure on the multiple and disorganized elements they were facing."[41] As a result, Löwy argues that their accounts take much into consideration but exclude "nearly everything related to the life of the inhabitants of zones of [yellow fever] endemicity…Sick persons and their families and neighbors are as a rule absent from narratives produced by the RF specialists, which are dominated by a quick-fix approach centered on the virus on the one hand and the *aegypti* larvae on the other."[42] Löwy's work is critical of the fact that while much attention is paid in these sources to detailing the features of communities and the ecology of Brazil in general, which supported the growth of a large and dangerous mosquito population, little recognition is paid to the significance of the social effects of a coffee-based economy, or to issues of social stratification, which may have produced difficult living circumstances. Quite pointedly, "...Brazil is frequently presented as a vast mosquito habitat and not much else".[43]

Chapter 3 End Notes

[1] Carrigan 1994; Sawchuk and Burke 1998.

[2] Hennen 1830, 60.

[3] If virus-harbouring mosquitoes arise in a community but bite only those who are immune, or the mosquitoes die before biting susceptible persons, the disease will not spread. If an infected person enters a community and is not bitten by a mosquito within the first three or four days of illness, the disease will not spread.

[4] Douglas Chester 1877.

[5] Based on Quarantine Proclamation of 1830, "Vessels coming from the West Indies, or that part of the Continent of America situated between the Equator and the 34th degree of N. lat and arriving between 1st July and 15th November shall forthwith quit Gibraltar." Page 49

[6] See Patterson 1992, 859.

[7] Benady 1994, 84.

[8] Patterson 1992, 855. It is also important to add that yellow fever could be over-reported due to cases of infective hepatitis or diarrhoea being classed as mild yellow fever during an epidemic.

[9] Patterson suggests that "men died in greater numbers than women, adults were more likely to contract fatal cases than children. Poor people seemed to be singled out in some epidemics, ..." (Patterson 1992, 860).

[10] Ellis 1992, 31.

[11] The figures represent all those who had passed through the fever by the end of the epidemic. This tabulation also provides insight into the scope and depth to which the yellow fever virus had penetrated the civilian population in Gibraltar (CO 91/103, Pym, Return of Persons who have and who have not passed the Epidemic Fevers in Gibraltar in the Year 1804, 1813, 1814 & 1828).

[12] During the course of the 1828 yellow fever epidemic the sick were compelled to enter the hospital for treatment.

[13] One can speculate that many of the men who entered the hospital may have been without familial caregivers.

[14] CO 91/100, Dated 1828 and signed Hugh Fraser, Surgeon. Note only 30 individuals are shown here.

[15] The chi-square value was 0.972 and p=0.615.

[16] Such claims have been echoed by Augustin 1909, 538; Everett 1950, 391; Goodyear 1978, 6; Patterson 1992, 860. There is at least one study that did not support this claim (Pritchett and Tunali 1995, 525-26).

[17]The sex ratio of individuals aged ten and older was 96.29 males for every 100 females (Nm=4,364 and Nf=4,532).

[18]There may be some error in the absolute magnitude of monthly death rates as we are using the 1834 census figures as a baseline (denominator) in the computation of these rates.

[19]In order to minimize any potential age bias (that is, young individuals being less susceptible to yellow fever), only deaths of individuals 10 years of age and older were considered in the statistical analysis.

[20]CO 91/103. Don to Murray, November 22, 1829.

[21]There is some suggestion from Gibraltar's former PMO, W.W. Fraser, that the military benefited from a more privileged set of circumstances during the course of an epidemic, including: moderate military discipline and exercise, the instant removal of the sick, whether men, women or children, frequent visits of military officers to hospitals, and the affording of liberal assistance to the sick by numerous orderlies (Fraser 1830).

[22]CO 91/103, Response by Dr. Wilson to query regarding water supply in Gibraltar in the Proceedings on the Origin of Yellow Fever in Gibraltar 1829.

[23]Walsh 1803, 7.

[24]The military population was, at all times, placed on a water allowance just as if the garrison was in a state of siege.

[25]Sawchuk, Burke and Padiak 2002.

[26]WO 334/12, Statement of deaths during the Yellow Fever Epidemic at Gibraltar from the 1st September 1828 to the 14th January 1829.

[27]WO 334/12, Statement of deaths during the Yellow Fever Epidemic at Gibraltar from the 1st September 1828 to the 14th January 1829.

[28]Herring and Swedlund 2003.

[29]Pritchett and Tunali 1995.

[30]Tunali and Pritchett 1997.

[31]Pritchett and Tunali 1995, 518.

[32]Pritchett and Tunali 1995, 518.

[33]Tunali and Pritchett 1997.

[34]Pritchett and Tunali 1995.

[35]Chalhoub 1993.

[36]Chalhoub 1993, 442.

[37]Chalhoub 1993, 442.

[38]Chalhoub 1993, 442.

[39]The disease was imported with mosquitoes which traveled aboard a ship recently returned from Cuba.

[41]Löwy 1997, 414.
[42]Löwy 1997, 414.
[43]Löwy 1997, 414.

– 4 –

The Impact of an Epidemic

THE LANDING PLACE

Coping with Crisis

From accounts taken after the epidemic of 1828, we learn that a number
of different strategies were used by the civilian residents to abate the
disease. These included: (1) fumigation, (2) whitewashing the houses,
(3) washing the furniture with rum, (4) changing clothes upon return-
ing from shopping in the village market, (5) sending servants into town
to do the shopping, (6) dousing the mail in vinegar, (7) not receiving

visitors into the home, (8) speaking through or by windows, (9) not taking anyone by the hand, and (10) separating families members who had passed through the fever from those who had not. The significance of these latter six strategies in combating the spread of a viral disease from mosquitoes is highly debatable but, perhaps more important, they may have played a role in lessening the fear and anxiety which people felt in the face of an epidemic disease.[1]

For some, flight was the answer. For the rich, the most obvious viable survival strategy would be to flee to an area with no (known) cases of yellow fever. In the case of Gibraltar, those who could afford it fled deep into isolated portions of the Spanish countryside, or to more distant locales (for example, England). Some would choose to take up residence on hulks anchored in the Bay. In stark contrast, the poor were in no position to escape without funds for travel, food, and lodging. Without voice or means, the poor were forced to live on charity and under conditions set by the authorities.

Travel in the Time of Epidemics

A state of quarantine not only impeded the free flow of goods, but it also proved a great inconvenience for travellers. This was particularly problematic for individuals travelling by sea. The state of quarantine circa 1824 was experienced first-hand by the American traveller, Theodore Dwight, who described the scene after entering the bay of Gibraltar:

> We had hardly come to anchor, when a boat came along side, a dark-complexioned man, with a sort of uniform dress, demanded in broken English, whence we came. He was the health officer; and his boatmen wore glazed hats marked G.R. The papers which were handed then, were taken with a pair of tongs, immersed in water, and then spread, by means of the boat's tiller and some sticks, for the officer to read; for we were in quarantine, we were treated exactly as if we had actually had the plague on board. We were to remain in quarantine two or three days; and our ensign being hauled

down, we hoisted a white flag.[2]

Another American traveler on board a vessel from Boston echoed this description three years later, though this observer was less charitable in his description of events; he complained of the prolonged state of quarantine imposed on his ship because it carried six cases of silk, arbitrarily judged to be of questionable origin. While the confinement onboard the ship was sufficiently irksome, it was the subjective power of the Health Officer that provoked an angry reaction from the traveler, who determined the physician's character to be offensive, supercilious, and rude.[3]

Hospital Care

Under the burden of coping with thousands sick during the yellow fever epidemics of 1804 and 1813/1814, it became painfully clear that medical facilities for the civilian population were woefully inadequate.[4] To meet the medical needs of the civilians, a committee, in co-operation with Lieutenant-Governor Don, built a hospital in 1815.[5] Hospital care was provided for both in- and out-patients. The Hospital Dispensary was open daily to out-patients, providing them with advice, medicines, and vaccinations.[6]

At the time of the 1828 epidemic, the Surgeon was Hugh Fraser, and the Assistant Surgeon and Purveyor was Peter Wilson.[7] Approximately 30 medical men, military and civilian, served the medical needs of the 20,000 inhabitants of the Rock. At the height of the 1828 epidemic, extra hospitals were crucial, and the partly built Protestant Church became Auxiliary Hospital No. 1, and the Methodist Chapel also became a temporary hospital.

To serve the military stationed in Gibraltar, there was the Naval Hospital. Built in 1746 and originally reserved for the use of the Navy, the hospital had largely been taken over by the Army after the end of the

Napoleonic Wars, and was referred to as the Military Hospital in the daily fever returns published in the *Gibraltar Chronicle*. It was in the charge of the Principal Medical Officer, who also had overall responsibility for the medical needs of the whole of Gibraltar. There were also a number of small Regimental Hospitals.

PROTESTANT CHURCH (MODIFIED FROM TRAVELLER'S HANDBOOK)

While a number of medical facilities existed in Gibraltar circa 1828, not all of Gibraltar's inhabitants were convinced of the curative value of hospitals. In fact, many perceived these as institutions of last resort, serving the destitute and those who had run out of hope. Such a view was not unique to Gibraltar; in the 19th century, hospitals were often regarded as "hotbeds of infection" or "gateways to death."[8] In Gibraltar, there was also a general reluctance of the poor to use the services of the English medical men[9] who were seen as outsiders, unable to communicate with locals in their native tongue, be it Spanish, Portuguese, or Genoese. Kelaart observed, "perhaps no class of people object to go into the hospital more than the poor of Gibraltar; and it is only when it is hopeless, or when the supply is stopped, that they can be persuaded to enter the hospital."[10] Further, the working classes were less likely to use the services of a physician because of the issue of payment. One report indicated that a single visit from a doctor would cost a working class family a week's wages.[11] When yellow fever struck, however, the cost of medical care and medicine was waived.

During the time of the yellow fever epidemics, the sick were compelled to enter the hospital and receive free treatment. The results of an analysis based on 459 patients with yellow fever compiled at the end of the 1828 epidemic are presented in the Table 14 below.

Table 14 indicates that the majority of the civilians who died of yellow fever died at home and not in the hospital.[12] Further, those that contracted yellow fever typically remained at home for 2 days before entering the hospital. Based on the hospital returns, the case fatality rate was 355 per 1000 [163 out of 459].

Time	Average	Min & Max
Sick before entering hospital	*2.15 days*	*1 to 24 days*
Total duration sick	*8.99 days*	*3 to 39 days*
Patients	*Number*	*Percent*
Males	*345*	*75*
Females	*114*	*25*
Jews	*42*	*91*
Non-Jews	*417*	*9*
Died	*296*	*64*
Survived	*163*	*36*

TABLE 14 STATISTICS ON YELLOW FEVER PATIENTS IN THE CIVIL HOSPITAL.

Long-term Consequences

The most immediate and obvious consequence of the epidemic was the tremendous loss of lives over a very brief period of time. One manifestation of this loss can be seen in the collective demographic profile of the individuals left behind at the time of the 1834 census, 6 years after the epidemic of 1828. The age-sex pyramid shown in Figure xx shows a conspicuous indentation in the profile of native-born individuals aged 30 and over; this reduction was caused by yellow fever deaths and emigration.

The social consequences of this loss were enormous; a great number of Gibraltar's inhabitants were left orphaned, widowed, or without kin. In a society like Gibraltar, where family ties are a key element of one's identity, the loss of kin would have devastating consequences on the social fabric of the community. This impact was further compounded by the loss of local knowledge and history accumulated by countless generations of Gibraltarians who survived sieges, starvation, and other major moments of crisis throughout the 18th century.

Costing an Epidemic

The cost of an epidemic can also be measured in economic terms. If there is one truism applicable to Gibraltar, it is that the economic fortunes of its inhabitants rose and fell with barometric regularity based on the amount of trade conducted, and obviously, epidemics were very bad for business. With the closing of all external communication with other countries, Gibraltar became isolated and, consequently, all sources of industry related to foreign-trade suffered as a result.[13] Resident foreigners involved in the trade of tobacco and British-manufactured cotton were thrown out of work, and one immediate repercussion was a reduction in the size of Gibraltar's alien community.[14] The wealthy also left the Rock, not in the hopes of securing employment, but to escape the ravages of disease. Some of the more affluent took temporary shelter in the Bay of Gibraltar or in the epidemic-free countryside in Spain.[15] Other local merchants and traders left permanently. The downturn in the economy rippled throughout the garrison and the commercial centre, causing great anxiety and concern. As businesses ceased operation, the poorer classes dependent on local commerce were deprived of all means of support.[16]

One direct measure of the cost to the poorer classes can be seen in a document created by the Inspectors of Districts, reproduced below, which reports that 4,822 individuals were economically distressed as a result of the epidemic. This number suggests that roughly one-third of the civilian population suffered immense hardship during the three month period that the epidemic was raging. It also appears that most of the charitable support went to the basic provisions: food, shelter, and clothing.

The plight of Gibraltar's inhabitants, both rich and poor, was further aggravated by the closing of the Spanish border during the epidemic. Being cut off from Spain meant that Gibraltarians would have to face an immediate and dramatic rise in food prices, as well as a shortage of imported food staples and goods. The impact on the local economy was so great that property values fell by an estimated 40 to 50 per-cent. The prosperity that once characterized Gibraltar in its halcyon days quickly disappeared in the shadow of the fever.

Preventative measures implemented during the epidemic must be fac-tored into the cost of any outbreak. There were considerable monies spent by the administration for the implementation of two measures considered (by them) to be essential for the security of the garrison's public health. In order to 'diminish the population' and 'cleanse the town', a total of £15,600 was expended: £8000 to establish a tem-porary village on the Neutral Ground; £4,515 for increased hospital expenditures caused by a rise in hospital admissions as well as in-creased outreach work in the form of expurgating infected houses and goods; £1,706 incurred in transporting water and other provisions to the troops; £1,046 to purchase spirits for the troops rather than the normal ration of wine; and finally, the sum of £343 for translating and copying the proceedings of the commission into the origins of yellow fever in Gibraltar.[17]

Treatment of Sex Workers

To outsiders, the treatment of civilians during an epidemic in Gi-braltar could be perceived as unduly harsh. However, it is important to emphasize that the British Empire understood Gibraltar to be first and foremost a military garrison town. Characteristic of a fortress, the garrison had limited permission of ingress, egress, and residence. With a garrison bounded by oppressive walls on all sides, the only way into or out of the town was through designated gates, continuously guarded by soldiers. The gates opened at daybreak and closed at dusk under normal conditions, which consequently controlled the movement of civilians. During epidemic times, these same gates would act as a barricade, preventing any escape from the ravages of disease.

One group of civilians who had little or no civil rights were Gibraltar's sex workers. Like many Garrison Towns throughout the British Empire, camp followers

EARLY 20TH CENTURY SEX WORKERS

or "prostitutes" were a common sight in Gibraltar. Throughout the 19th century, Gibraltar's sex workers were carefully monitored and highly regulated. During the epidemic of 1828, Gibraltar's authorities were quick to take action against the resident prostitutes. To prevent the possible spread of yellow fever through sexual contact, Gibraltar's authorities issued the following directive by the 6th of September,

> That the inspectors of Districts in company with the Police Sergeants, be directed to make a most minute inspection, and without the loss of time, to compel all the Garrison prostitutes, who remain in the Garrison to be transferred to the Camp on the on the Neutral Ground and on no pretence to be re-admitted until further orders.[18]

Obedience, orderliness, and control were the hallmarks of garrison life, and particularly for those who were engaged as prostitutes in times of disease.

Hiding the Sick and Dead

One axiom of any epidemic is that there will always be individuals who conceal or misrepresent cases of sickness and death. The situation in Gibraltar during the yellow fever visitations was no exception; both the public and authorities practiced this type of misrepresentation. While Sergeant Anton, who witnessed the 1828 epidemic, tells us that concealment was common at this time, Dr. Barry provides even more detailed information on this phenomenon:

> Two motives always actuate the Spaniard and the native of Gibraltar to conceal or dissimulate, by every possible artifice, the existence of yellow fever in their families. 1st To avoid the inconvenience of being sent into the lazaretto camp, and other sanitary annoyances. 2dly. As the older members of the family have generally acquired immunity for themselves, by having had the disease in some former epidemic, they are adverse to their children being deprived of the present opportunity of acquiring similar immunity, knowing that, at their age, the risk of death is less than it will be afterwards, if so exposed to infection.[19]

The poor were reluctant to report a contagious disease, since they risked losing what little property they had – it was common practice at the time for contaminated articles (e.g. clothes, mattresses) to be burned or otherwise destroyed or disposed of.

Colonel Bayly, stationed in Gibraltar during the 1828 epidemic, provides another instance where concealment was brought to the authorities' attention. Here he describes a case involving members of the Jewish community in Gibraltar:

> The dead-carts were continually parading the streets of the town to receive the corpses, which were interred without any ceremony. To avoid this contamination, a wealthy Jew had secreted ten bodies of his persuasion in a

large loft, in consequence of which the precincts of his habitation became absolutely doubly pestiferous from the sickening odours encircling it. The town major was soon informed of this abomination, and instantly dispatched a party of police for the purpose of removing the nuisance. The Jews, however, resisted this authority; the town major was therefore compelled to proceed with a party of the military, when ten bodies in a most putrid state of decomposition were deposited in a cart and conveyed to the usual cemetery;...[20]

The Jews preferred to inter their dead in a dedicated burial ground above Windmill Hill in the South.[21] Located about 3 miles from the Town, the Jews' cemetery was considered, by its community, to be a salubrious site and ideally placed. According to custom, bodies were buried without coffins. The corpse was first covered with stones and earth, and then a two-foot layer of stone and mortar was placed on top of the stratum. Each grave was limited to one person. The Jews

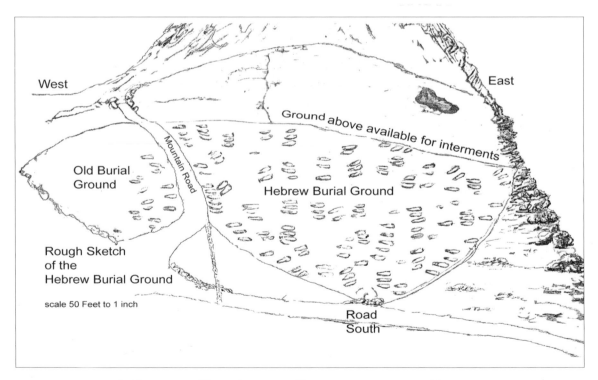

A PLAN OF THE JEWISH CEMETERY IN THE SOUTH

preferred the rocky site as it was judged improper to bury the dead in wet soil.

Authorities were frequently no less guilty of misrepresentation during the crisis. Consider a case in 1829, when six possible cases of yellow fever appeared in the Corps of Sappers, raising anxiety among the military and authorities; the Principal Medical Officer later confessed in a War Office document, "It was necessary, in order to prevent Spain and other nations from taking steps against us, in fear of contagion to be discreet in giving the Disease a name."

Searching for Scapegoats

One remarkable universal of global epidemic experiences is the singling out of a selected group (or groups) as the source or carrier of an infectious disease.[22] Scapegoating or demonizing a group invariably involves a minority group, usually recent immigrants; the practice stems out of ignorance, prejudice, or desperation. One of the earliest examples of fixing blame on 'the other' in Gibraltar dates back to 1804 when a public health commission attributed the outbreak of yellow fever to foreigners. In this particular instance, it was the Barbary Jews who were further singled out and reproached, as their 'habits and uncleanliness' were believed to have led to the spread of the disease. Here the

JEWISH PORTER (FROM A PRINT BY CARTER, T. BENADY)

newly-arrived outsider was the convenient scapegoat to target as the

187

source of disease. Similar misguided sentiments were expressed during the 1828 Gibraltar epidemic when a Westminster physician wrote in the influential medical journal Lancet,

> A disease presenting all the characters of an epidemic malady, was seen in several cases of the autumn months of 1825, 1826, and 1827. These occurred principally in the filthy habitations of the poor Jews, who were crowded together in an incredibly small space. The stench of their dormitories at night was intolerably offensive, and abundantly sufficient to produce in persons even in good constitution, a fever of no slight type.[23]

The lack of hygiene, overcrowding, and perceived poor moral character unfairly attributed to the poor Jewish immigrants were all qualities that were thought of as factors that facilitated the spread of diseases like yellow fever. All too often colonial authorities were unwilling to admit that Gibraltar itself could be the source of contagion, since this admission could damage both the perception of military strength and readiness as well as threaten commercial relations. Admitting a local source of contagion would also lead to the most intuitive next step – costly measures of clean-up. As a result, scapegoating and, in particular, ascribing blame to 'outsiders' or the newly-arrived immigrant remained the most convenient and economically sound explanation for an outbreak of disease.

Finding scapegoats was not difficult within Gibraltar, given the fact that it did attract a large and diverse population; isolating scapegoats within a general colonial context was also not difficult, since there was usually a large and insurmountable social distance that existed between the colonizer and the colonized. Examining the effects of the 1878 yellow fever epidemic on the French colony of Saint-Louis-du-Sénégal, Ngalamulume finds ample evidence that the local population was more often held responsible, either directly or indirectly, for the colony's misfortunes since "in French thinking, the indigènes had disqualified themselves from sanitary citizenship by refusing to adopt

French cultural values and ideas of progress."[24]   When the 1878 epidemic arrived in Saint-Louis in September of that year, the devastation that followed in its wake motivated local authorities to consider quar antine measures, to remove the foreign floating population resident in the city, to send all non-essential French persons back to Europe, and to completely remove all indigènes from the city. Even as late as 1901, Ngalamulume found evidence that authorities considered the "sanitary segregation" of indigènes and colonial troops. Despite all of these con templated measures, the only real success in controlling yellow fever in Saint-Louis had little to do with people and more to do with controlling the local mosquito population, particularly in and around the swampy areas located in close proximity to the city.

A Trial is Postponed

The postponing and cancellation of another public events represented another universal feature of life during an epidemic. One of the more unusual examples of this phenomenon involves the trial of a notorious pirate, Benito de Soto, which had to be delayed until the cessation of the epidemic.

BENITO SOTO

Benito de Soto, mate of the brig El Defensor de Pedro, was indicted for piratical behaviour involving the English ship, Morning Star, on the 19th February 1828. After a failed attempt to profit from the ship's bounty off of the coast of Cadiz, Benito fled to Gibraltar to escape Spanish authorities. Using a fake pass, he entered the gates of Gibraltar on the 26th May 1828. Evidence given at his trial indicates that he remained at large in the garrison for 41 days, and that his permit of residence was renewed twice.

After his capture in Gibraltar in June of 1828, he was held for trial. To ensure that a proper and fair hearing was held, testimony from witnesses who could identify and provide evidence against de Soto was mandatory. A raging epidemic made travel to Gibraltar impossible and, accordingly, the trial proceedings had to be delayed. After a pro-tracted period of incarceration, de Soto was finally tried at the Admiralty Session of the Peace on the 13th of January 1830, found guilty and sentenced to be hanged. Ironically, his fate was met on the same grounds that earlier offered hope and relief from the dreaded yellow fever,

> At nine o'clock on the morning of January 25th [1830], five days after his trial, Benito de Soto was brought from the Moorish Castle escorted by the Provost Marshal and a small guard, to the place of execution. Attended by a Spanish priest, he walked slowly at the tail of the car, on which was his coffin. He held a Crucifix in his hand, from which he scarcely ever raised his eyes, and frequently kissed it with apparent devotion. On his arrival at the fatal spot, which was fronting the Neutral Ground, and the verge of the bay, he spent a quarter of an hour in fervent prayer, the rain falling heavily all the time. At the final moment, he mounted the car firmly, and harangued the surrounding populace in Spanish acknowledging the justice of his sentence, and exhorting them to take warning by his death, and to pray for him. He endeavoured to assist the executioner in performing his awful duty. Finding the halter too high, he boldly stepped upon his coffin and placed his neck to the noose. Then, as the car drew away, he leaned forward - sprang, as to assist the impetus of his fall - and passed into eternity without the slightest struggle.

The Findings of the Commission

After the epidemic had ceased, two Commissions of Enquiry were con-vened: one military, chaired by Sir William Pym, the other was most ly civilian, and largely dominated by the three French physicians sent over by the Paris Academy of Sciences[25] to study the epidemic. A summary of the latter Commission's findings (presented below) speaks to the state of knowledge about causation of the yellow fever epidemic at that time,

> In the investigation of this question we shall avoid all discussion as to the nature of the Fever, premising however, as a general principle, that Fevers may and do   often arise from local causes, and although perhaps not contagious or infectious at the time of their origin may become so as their progress; We also admit that Fever may be imported by means of vessels; we shall therefore confine ourselves to the exploration of the Quarantine, and there is the testimony of the Captain of the Port that the Fever do not exist on board of any vessel in the Bay during the summer and autumn of 1828.

> On the other had, it appears to us to be established by the evidence of many individuals of competent judgment and high respectability that a very dense   pauper population did exist in many parts of the Town of Gibraltar in the year 1828, and that they inhabited ill ventilated and crowded apartments; that in consequence of the decay of trade, wages were low and the comforts of the working classes, both as regards food and clothing were course diminished; water for personal cleanliness and other purposes was also scarce; and the drains and privies and sewers emitted an offensive smell, in the opinion of highly respectable individuals more so than in preceding years.

> Believing that a dense Population probably badly fed and clothed and living in crowded or ill ventilated apartments suffering under a scanty supply of water under a high temperature and a defective circulation of the atmosphere are causes very likely to produce Fever of an infectious or contagious nature, we incline to the opinion that disease was of local origin; probably not contagious at first, but becoming during its progress highly so in Gibraltar, but apparently not easily communicable on the Neutral Ground. It is true that there is evidence to shew that the aggregate population was not higher but perhaps lower in 1828, and it is also stated by the individual who had the charge of the sewers, that the state of drains and sewers was not worst than years preceding 1828 and that the houses were not more crowded, but the Provost states that some houses were dilapidated

and the comfort of the poor population was less than in former years.

Every one seems to admit the existence of a dense population – offensive smells from the drains and sewers and defect of water to carry off filth, and there is positive evidence of Dr. Hennen and Dr. Fraser – of Col. Pearson and of others that about the time the FEVER first appeared some houses and apartments in District 24 where the Fever is said to have first appeared were crowded and badly ventilated and filthy, and these gentlemen speak positively to these facts, which come under their own observation and perhaps their evidence may be fairly deemed more important than those that of persons who from habit had become familiar to crowded apartments and offensive smells, and perhaps, omitted to report the state of their Districts so accurately as they ought to have done.

The origin of this dreadful disease being uncertain, it seems to be prudent to use precautions to prevent its recurrence, whether imported or of local origin. In order to prevent its being introduced by means of vessels, we recommended strict attention to the Quarantine laws; if any defects should be found to exist, they should be remedied; the utmost care is required that they should be carefully and rigidly enforced; this is peculiarly requisite at Gibraltar which, from want of space is ill adapted for a Quarantine Station.

In order to prevent its recurrence of the disease from local causes we beg to leave to recommend a rigid attention to the Police of the Town. The Police Regulations we believe to be well formed but we fear that they have not been strictly executed at all times, too much appears to have been left to the Police Serjeants, we therefore suggest the appointment of a Board of Competent persons to superintend the Police and that a Medical Officer should be appointed Superintendant of Police with a Salary, whose duty it should be to visit frequently all parts of the Town. He should be responsible for the state of the habitations of the lower class of people, and should have power to enter all lodging houses, in order to ascertain the number of inmates in each apartment and should make periodical reports to the Board.

As we consider well constructed drains and sewers and an abundant supply of water to be very conducive to the healthiness of a Town, we beg to suggest that the drains and sewers be examined by competent judges, and as fresh water is much too scarce in the dry season at Gibraltar to be supplied in sufficient quantity for the purposes of carrying off filth, we think that to the investigation of the evidence of the Proceedings of the Board of Enquiry held at Gibraltar to enquire into the origin of the Fever. After having carefully minutely read over these minutes with our minds, we trust unbiased by any theory or hypothesis, we cannot assent to the opinion that the Fever was imported either by means of the Dygden or by any other vessel as there is not sufficient evidence to prove that any contagious disease existed on board the Dygden during the timer that vessel was in Quarantine in the Bay of Gibraltar, nor is there any valid evidence to prove that contagious fever existed during existed during the summer or autumn on board any vessel in the Bay of Gibraltar. On the contrary, there is the direct testimony of the late Dr. Hennen that the crew of Dygden were in perfect health, when the vessel was placed in Quarantine and also when examined by him out the place which has been suggested as raising sea water by means of steam engine into reservoirs should be adopted; and that the drains should have a decent toward the main sewers, which should we carried along the beach beyond low water mark, and a current of sea water should be thrown into the drains and sewers to carry the contents of them into the sea.

As it appears probable if not certain, that the Fever was not contagious on the Neutral Ground, we beg to suggest that Buildings, either temporary or permanent (as circumstances may permit) should be erected upon the neutral ground to which ill cases of fever should b e immediately conveyed; there should be three Buildings, one for observation, another for decided cases of fever, and a third for Convalescents.

The poor to be treated free of expense; more opulent persons might pay for the accommodation they should be desirous of receiving.

The Question fo Causation Remains Unanswered

The 1828 Gibraltar yellow fever epidemic was neither the time nor the place for the development of a new scientific paradigm. These enquiries did little to resolve fundamental etiological or epidemiological questions relating to yellow fever. Nor did these enquiries resolve precisely which administrative measures might be useful in preventing future epidemics.

This is not surprising, as the basis for a rigorous scientific investigation of disease and the disease process were completely lacking at this time. Knowledge of the basic principles of the germ theory would still be another fifty odd years away with the work of Pasteur, among others. At this time, there was no clear understanding of yellow fever as a distinct clinical entity that could aid physicians in differentiating it from other similar diseases. Another missing prerequisite was any mandate encouraging the collection of information on all of the individuals exposed to infection, not simply those that became sick and/or died. The opportunity of early detection of the index case was also lost, as investigators waited two months after the outbreak to reconstruct the origin and the pattern of disease transmission. While Hennen advocated the implementation of a Board of Inquiry into the origin of the epidemic early into the outbreak, Lieutenant-Governor Don did not support this request,

> I have declined granting this Board at the present junction as the minds and attention of all are fully occupied by the existing calamity. I confess I am of the opinion that the most satisfactory mode of investigating this important matter would be by a board of competent persons sent from England as being uninfluenced by local feelings.[26]

Imperfect memories also served to confuse and obfuscate any clear understanding of the progress of the disease. Concealment of the sick by friends and families contributed to keeping the chain of infection a mystery. Finally, long-standing personal biases and prejudice of the investigators themselves ensured that the disease would remain an enigma. On this final note, it is fitting to restate Lieutenant-Governor Don's sentiments on the merit of the Gibraltar Enquiry:

> On the subject of the Proceedings of the Board of Enquiry into the Origin of the Fever, I cannot refer to them as the result of an impartial, unbi-

ased investigation of facts, because the desire to establish or confirm particular doctrines and opinions gave rise to a strong party feeling in which I believe, few did not participate, and I sincerely hope, that you will not be induced to rely implicitly on the evidence given, or the opinions expressed to the Board under such circumstances.[27]

While one can question the impartiality and corresponding value of the commission's findings, there can be little disagreement that the yellow fever epidemics served as the primary stimulus in the development of stricter quarantine measures, as well as the beginning of sanitary and medical reform. At the beginning of the 19th century, Gibraltar had the notorious reputation as the dirtiest garrison under the British Crown, because of its filth and lack of paved streets, garbage collection, or adequate sewage facilities. Deplorable housing was the norm, with stables and sheds for cattle and horses mixed with civilian houses. There was no Civil Hospital established for the reception of the impoverished sick. There was also no system established for the surveillance of the health of the civil population. Immigration was lax and largely unmonitored. Food markets were badly regulated, and there was little control over the quality of the food sold. Under the enlightened stewardship of Lieutenant-Governor Don, Gibraltar's sanitary and medical infrastructure took the first step on the path to reform. The great fever epidemics were the deadly catalysts that set these reforms in motion.

The Legacy of the Great Fevers

In attempting to reconstruct the history of a people, we face the daunting task of deciphering the accumulation of countless events operating within the fundamental forces of nature and the human condition. Our appreciation of any human community at given point in time can narrowly be seen as a function of comprehending a set of normalizing background conditions as well as product of moments of crisis as they collectively reshuffle the properties of a population in ways that are both deterministic and random. It is this unusual set of events and forces that make a community distinctive and generate a feeling of "us" and "them". Our focus in this book has been to capture one moment of crisis brought about by an epidemic and how an array of normally invisible features of society are crystallized and surface in a vast panorama of vignettes that speak to the inherent complexity that are involved in the making of a people. Recall that the identity of any community is a complex dynamic process that is shaped by historical events that impact on a group of individuals. This group perceives themselves as one by virtue of sharing a common background in terms of their biology, social and cultural properties, and demography within a given environmental background. This distinctiveness is reinforced by participating in a myriad of social interactions (such as marriage, speaking a common language and so forth) as well as establishing boundaries to identify "other' from 'us'. In this way people recognize themselves as distinctive ethnic or cultural groups. Studying the history of a community can provide the researcher important clues as to which events and forces were instrumental in shaping group identity. It is our contention that the Gibraltarian character or ethos was crystallized in times of adversity and moments of crisis. Further, we posit that the 'Gibraltarian' identity was fundamentally shaped by the events of the early 18th century and in particular, serial episodes of yellow fever that struck the community with great ferocity.

To support our proposition, we will concentrate on one human facet that persists over long periods of time, the biological or genetic makeup of a people. Recently, students of human evolution have begun to appreciate and look at epidemics as forces capable of producing sig- nificant and long-term change. Under a commonly accepted scenario for biological change through infectious diseases there are three factors necessary for natural selection to operate. The first criterion is that the infectious disease in question is capable of killing individuals before the end of the reproductive period and/

or interfering with the reproductive capabilities of an individual. The second factor is variation, where individuals in a population who possess a particular genetic endowment are more fit than other individuals lacking that particular genetic makeup. Here natural selection may operate through differential mortality and/or through differential fertility associated with a given genotypes which acts to 'select for' or 'against' specific genotypes. Finally, the disease must be persistent over time (that is a series of an epidemic or better yet that the disease is endemic) as selection typically requires many generations to produce any long-term effects. Lacking a clear understanding if, in fact, there was a specific gene involved in increased resistance or susceptibility, we will argue how biological change may have occurred without fulfilling the commonly accepted criteria stated above.

When yellow fever struck the population in 1804, one result was that the population underwent a dramatic reduction in number leaving behind only those who survived the epidemic. The survivors were thus granted life-long immunity against future attacks of yellow fever. While there may have been a gene complex underlying survivorship, at this moment it is impossible to know with any certainty. What is known is that after 1804 thousands of individuals poured into Gibraltar to fill the void left after the epidemic. Some of these individuals were likely the survivors of the same yellow fever epidemic that raged throughout the Iberian peninsula in 1804. In other words, there may have been a form of social selection operating to encourage those who had acquired immunity to settle in Gibraltar knowing that they would be not liable to a second attack. The epidemics of 1813, 1814 and 1828 continued to select for those who survived previous epidemics or who by some a particular quality who could survive an attack of yellow fever. The argument here is that yellow fever acted as a magnet drawing yellow fever survivors and repelling those who had not yet passed the fever. We suggest one factor for some that factored into whether individuals emigrated from non-fever localities to high a location of "high risk' where the etiology of the disease was unknown and there was no effective therapy. However, it can also be argued that life at the time was nasty, brutish and short for many other reasons, only some of them diseases, so the fear of yellow fever in Gibraltar can have been only a minor consideration, if it was considered at all (see Figure 12).

Nonetheless it is clear that migrants from the surrounding Spanish countryside and other localities in the Mediterranean found a safe haven from political persecution, year around employment, marriage opportunities to the natives and, for the young and reckless, quick profit through smuggling and profiteering. By the early 19th century, the quite small garrison town of Gibraltar with its civilian population began to reap the economic rewards of its unique geo-political position and the opportunity for trade afforded by Napoleon's Continental System would have been far more prominent, and the vacuum left behind by those who had emigrated or succumbed to the great fevers. In summary, the serial episodes of yellow fever epidemics that struck the Rock provided the opportunity for a dramatic demographic replacement of the population at an unprecedented level. It was these new founders in concert with the indigenous inhabitants then thus served as the nucleus for the stimulus and growth of the future Gibraltarian identity.

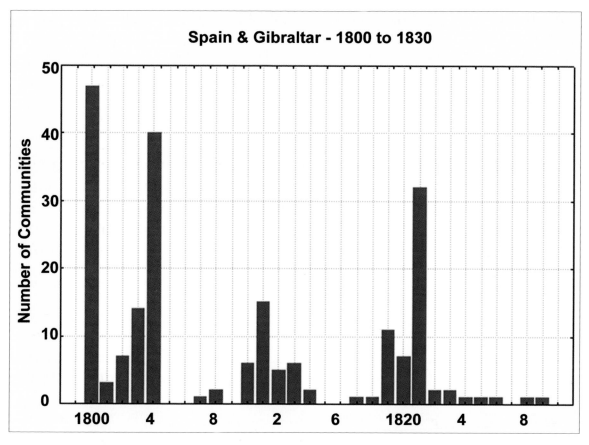

FIGURE 12. YELLOW FEVER - NUMBER OF INFECTED LOCALITIES

Chapter Four Endnotes:

[1]From a board of inquiry, conducted by Barry and the well known French Medical Commissioners,

[2]Dwight 1824, 10-11. It is likely that traveler was not aware that the papers were immersed in container of vinegar and water, rather than water alone.

[3]"At a certain hour each day, the health Physician, an examiner would go on board ships at Gibraltar. A signal flag is displayed. Boats from the ships in quarantine then put off to it for the purpose of communication, but are not suffered to approach within a certain distance. The Health Officer was described as a dapper looking doctor reclining in a comfortable armchair placed on the quarterdeck" (Bigelow 1831, 30-32).

[4]Until 1815, care of the sick in Gibraltar was in the hands of private and independent physicians. The sick were "lodged in hired houses, at heavy expense, where they are badly accommodated, and frequently at a distance from the Medical Officer."

[5]It is noteworthy that the hospital was separated along religious lines and not according to illness.

[6]In non-epidemic times we learn that over a period of ten years, namely, from its first establishment in 1815, to 20th December, 1825, there were 2,333 cases treated in the hospital and 13,182 out-patients (Hennen 1830, 91).

[7]Wilson spent 14 years in Gibraltar. ADM 105/20. P. Wilson, Surgeon, to Sir George Warrender Bart. Dunbar, August 23, 1832. page 174. He was fired in early 1829 when he disobeyed an order to remain in Gibraltar to give evidence to the Commission of Enquiry.

[8]A more charitable and less pessimistic perspective has been put forward by Cherry 1980.

[9]The development and promotion of an English medical system in Gibraltar can also be seen as the by-product of a colonial agenda that discouraged the presence of non-British physicians on the Rock. For more on the subject of colonial medicine, see Arnold 1993; Cooper and Stoler 1997; Marks 1997.

[10]Keelart 1846, 44.

[11]A labourer earning a maximum of 25 pesetas a week would be reluctant to call in a doctor whose fee for a single visit amounted to more than a whole week's wages. Spanish doctors, on the other hand, charged considerably less.

[12]1170 died in total -163 in hospital and 1007 at home.

[13]Cottons, woollens, linens and silks from England and France were re-exported to Spain and Morocco. Sugar from Cuba and Brazilian coffee beans were sent

to Morocco. Corn and seeds from Morocco were sent to England, while metals from England were exported to Spain, Portugal and Morocco. Wool and hides from Morocco were shipped to England, France, Italy and the United States.

[14]CO 91/103, September 17, 1829. Cadiz is mentioned in a despatch from Don to Murray as a location where these foreigners could find similar employment.

[15]For the majority of the lower class there was no other option but to remain and face whatever consequences were to follow. Unlike other larger dominions where flight to the hinterland was a possibility, the inhabitants of Gibraltar were virtually prisoners within their own walls. Flight in the face of an epidemic was a luxury that only the wealthy, privileged and connected could afford. Note also, that Jews were not allowed into Spain - cf. T Benady: Aaron Cardozo, Life and Letters G Books 004, pxi

[16]Tobacco was generally the most important commodity creating employment opportunities for the labouring population. Approximately 1,700 men, women and children were engaged in Gibraltar's tobacco trade. Of these, about 90% were native Gibraltarian.

[17]CO 91/103. An explanation of expenditures for services which occurred during the epidemic. Don to Murray, November 22, 1829.

[18]Inspector's Office. Gibraltar 6 Sept 1828.

[19]Barry 1830, 13. Recall that the literature suggests that children seem to have a stronger resistance to the virus and generally suffer only mild or sub-clinical cases.

[20]Bayly 1896, 275.

[21]All funerals were alike without distinction of wealth or station. If necessary, the expense of funerals were defrayed from public funds.

[22]For example, McGrew (1962) reports that during the 1831 epidemic in Russia, cholera deaths were blamed on foreigners in general, and Poles and Germans in particular. For a discussion of anti-Semitism, scapegoating and cholera in Hamburg, see Evans (1987). For other examples of demonising the Jews in Gibraltar see Sawchuk and Burke 1998; Sawchuk, 2001

[23]Edwards 1830.

[24]Ngalamulume 2004, 191.

[25]Documents recueillis par M.M. Chervin, Louis et Trousseau, membres de la commission Francaise envoyée a Gibraltar pour observer l'épidémie de 1828; et par M. le Dr. Barry, médecin des armies anglaises, 2 vols. (Paris: Imprimerie royale, 1830).

[26]GGA Miscellaneous Papers. Don to Sir George Murray, September 22, 1828.

[27]CO 91/103. Don to Sir George Murray, November 22, 1829.

– 5 –

Contextualizing The Epidemic Experience In Colonial Times

THE KINGS BASTION

Colonial Identity and Fortress Mentality

Gibraltar was part of the British Colonial Empire as well as a fortified garrison town. It was this long-term residence within a fortress that shaped the character of its inhabitants, and imposed yet another level of social and political control over a colonized people. A characterization of the pervasive quality of garrison living has been termed a 'fortress mentality'. In the case of Gibraltar, the development of a fortress mentality was a multifaceted response, not only to life within the confines of a fortress, but also its unique geo-political location, and its unusual colonial status. Civilians were regarded as secondary citizens or subordinate civilians living on sufferance. Time and again, the administration reiterated that the sole purpose of a civilian presence on the Rock was to serve as the unquestioning instrument of the Empire. The comments provided by one colonial official illustrate the nature and underlying tone of this relationship:

> it should be remembered that the raison d'etre of this colony is as a fortress; from any other than a strategic point of view its existence is absolute encumbrance to the empire; and under this aspect it is monstrous that in addition to the want of provision for the civilian safety the strategic necessities for which Gibraltar exists at so great expense to the imperial government should be imperiled and the health of the troops exposed to serious risk by the negligence of the civil community; and so although under ordinary circumstances the civil population which has grown up under the shelter of the walls is entitled to every consideration and privilege attaching to their status as British subjects, it must be conceded by the most prejudiced that, as in time of war, so in time of general sickness, the civil must for the common well of both, become subservient to the military element...[1]

Similar sentiments resonated throughout the British Empire, where civilians lived within colonial fortresses. The Maltese, like their Gibraltarian counterparts, were also regarded as secondary to military needs. Admiral Sir John Fisher wrote in a memorandum at the turn of the century that Malta existed solely for the Navy,

> For imperial purposes, it has no value whatever. It produces nothing. It has no manufacturers. .... Malta possesses no military value whatever; it exists for the Navy; and it exists by the Navy. ... Malta is a fortress, pure and simple, and should be governed as a Fortress.[2]

Control was exercised by a military governor who had complete power; civilians had absolutely no influence in the appointment of their ruler. Gibraltarians were for the most part politically powerless. Laws governing local affairs were handed down as ordinances which the local inhabitants had little opportunity to shape or influence (see Figure 13).

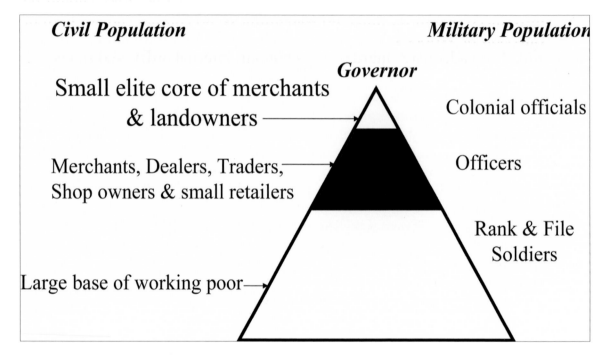

FIGURE 13. GIBRALTAR'S INHABITANTS

There was "no constitutional machinery whatsoever to ensure that no law is enacted which is contrary to the wishes of the majority of the people."[3] This longstanding experience of powerlessness among the civilians gradually shaped the Gibraltarian identity and ultimately became part of their ethos.

The power of the military Governor extended into virtually every element of daily life. The breadth of this control over civilian affairs was enormous and reinforced by the lack of a free, uncontrolled press.[4]

The Administration's position on the matter of freedom of the press was clear:

> There is no Gem in the British Crown of more Imperial value than the Fortress of Gibraltar. With due vigilance against all adversary combinations, avowed or secret; but if a free, wild, uncensored press should be introduced within its walls, no watchfulness, no courage, no strength of Garrison or Works, could prevent the subversion of its moral securities and afford adequate Guard over its honour, internal order, and safety.[5]

For much of the 19th century in Gibraltar the only local newspaper, the *Gibraltar Chronicle,* was "the medium of publication of all Government notices ... only public notices and acts appearing in the Chronicle signed by the proper authorities are to be considered official."[6] Censorship was rigid, with an editor appointed by and acting under the control of the Garrison Library, of which the Major General was invariably chosen as President. No political journal was to be tolerated. No statements from political refugees or malcontents were to be published. Opposition to government policies in the time of peace or in crisis was totally unacceptable. Gibraltar, like Malta, was a fortress, and "anything like open agitation" could not, and would not, be tolerated.[7]

The Gibraltarian character was not solely influenced by political status, but also shaped by the physical topography of a fortified garrison, with its imposing limestone backdrop, its heavily fortified confining walls, and limited habitable space. Gibraltar was described as having "no public buildings of architectural importance; ... a fortified post, in which art and beauty are subordinate to the useful."[8] This was the day-to-day scene pressed into the minds of the civilian inhabitants of the Rock. With an extensive series of barracks for housing soldiers throughout the town and territory, one could not escape the military presence of the town. The military parade-ground was located within the town and its daily regimented activities reinforced the fact that Gibraltar was primarily a garrison town. Within the walled confines of the city, the deafening cry of sergeants' commands and processions of soldiers marching down narrow streets served as a constant reminder of order, discipline, and position. The words of a visitor to the Rock testifies to the quality of life in the fortress,

> Here the military element is so absorbing and controlling, that it dominates the whole life of the place. Everything goes by military rule, even the hours of the day are announced by "gun fire", the morning gun gives the exact minute at which the soldiers are to turn out of their beds, and the last evening gun the minute at which they are to "turn in", signals which, though for the soldiers only, the working population of the town find it convenient to adapt; and which outsiders must regard, since at these hours the gates are opened and shut; so that a large part of the non military part of the population has to "keep step", almost as much as if they were marching in the ranks.[9]

The imposition of the military on civilian affairs was one of strict social control. Control spread into restrictions with respect to where civilian housing could be located, stringent limitations on the height of buildings, and direct competition for scarce resources, such as housing and water supplies. While the fortress walls were seen as defensive barriers against the unwelcome, they also served as a powerful force of domination over local residents. Civilians were not given free movement within a garrison town; every action was carefully monitored by the Police and District Inspectors. Even the right to be out at night was regulated by special passes. Life was so rigid, civilians were not even allowed to draw or sketch with Gibraltar's walls since concern for military security reigned paramount. Specific ordinances were passed to prevent civilians from drawing their surroundings, an activity otherwise considered a normal past-time in most societies.

From the perspective of the military administration, Gibraltar and its inhabitants were an oddity and a singularity,

> Gibraltar is not a dominion or possession where Her Majesty's subjects are at full liberty to enter or reside in or wherein to hire or possess hous-

es or manufactures, warehouses, shops and premises or wherein to carry on their commerce. Military exigencies operating upon an area which affords no room for such purposes renders it simply impossible that it shall ever be so.[10]

The subordinate position of the indigenous population, and the preferential treatment of 'outsiders' from the British Empire in terms of position, housing, wages, and mobility reinforced the marginalization of the civilian community. Improvements to local health and sanitary infrastructure typically became a priority when there was a direct benefit to the garrisoned military forces. Unlike other British possessions settled by colonists, the administration considered Gibraltarians,

> ... not colonists in the true sense of that word. They are substantially part of the garrison that is both British subjects permitted to reside for the purpose of supplying the rest of the Garrison with such necessary provisions and as such are imported from a distance and their employee's domestic servants, camp followers and civil officers.[11]

Civilians were not only treated as a source of cheap labour, but they were also regarded by the colonial administration as a real and potential threat to the security of the Rock. While wary of the Spanish pedigree of some of its inhabitants, the administration remained attentive to other threats – mainly the potential spread of deadly epidemics fromsecondary civilians who were "naturally uncleanly" in their habits and in their houses. Gibraltarians began to perceive themselves as a people apart, second-class citizens within their own homeland governed by outsiders. From the perspective of the Governor and his officials, the 'native' was a term that signified inferiority.

It was no exaggeration that daily life within the fortress walls could be stifling and conducive to feeling trapped. For the military, Gibraltar afforded few pleasures and for the civilians, daily life was no doubt equally as confining,

Gratis.

80 days.

No. _____

[NOTE.—Every temporary permit becomes void by the marriage of the Alien admitted and every Alien must immediately upon marriage leave Gibraltar, together with his wife whether she be an Alien, a Native, or other British nationality.]

TEMPORARY PERMIT.

NOT TRANSFERABLE.

POLICE OFFICE, GIBRALTAR,   18

Permission has been granted to   upon his application

and responsibility that   may enter and reside in Gibraltar

as a person unmarried, gaining her livelihood by occasional employment till the

189   , unless such permission shall be in the meantime revoked.

By command of His Excellency the Governor,

Chief of Police.

Extended the   day of   18   till the   18

Chief of Police.

Extended the   day of   18   till the   18

Chief of Police.

Extended the   day of   18   till the   18

Chief of Police.

[NOTICE.—This permit must, on or before the day when it will expire, be delivered up by the person abovementioned, as permitted to enter and reside in Gibraltar, on leaving the said fortress, to the Inspector of Police on duty at the barrier through which he shall so leave.]

I certify that the person above permitted to enter and reside in Gibraltar left the fortress by the

barrier on the   day of

Police Inspector.

ADVERTENCIA.—El individuo arriba mencionado deberá devolver la presente al Inspector de Policía que esté de servicio en la puerta por la cual salga de la guarnicion.

A TEMPORARY PERMIT

**STONE WALLS AND WEAPONS WERE PRESENT
THROUGHOUT GIBRALTAR**

The society of Gibraltar resembles the society of most garrison towns, the nature of which can be best understood by those who have at any time resided in one. There are few sources of amusement in Gibraltar. In vain will the lover of the fine arts seek to gratify his tastes. Opera and theatrical companies have very little support, and consequently their visits to the rock are few and far between. The officers keep a tolerably good pack of hounds, which is to them a great source of healthful enjoyment, and to the Spaniards one of astonishment. The races, too, come off with great *eclat*. Public balls are held in the winter, which serve to keep the young people amused.[12]

Since the British occupation of the Rock, the military and civilian communities have co-resided with minimal social interaction and little scope for integration.[13]

A Time When Colonies were Dangerous but Lucrative

Gibraltar was but one colony established by the British in its push for

colonial expansion. The British Empire, of course, expanded well beyond Gibraltar, with other British colonies established in such diverse
places as India, Cyprus, Malta, Canada, Africa, Australia, Jamaica,
and Barbados (some Caribbean islands remain British overseas territories today). Other significant colonizers were the Spanish (e.g.,
Mexico, Florida, Chile, Peru, Venezuela, Costa Rica, Guatemala), the
Portuguese (e.g., Brazil, Macao, Azores, Cape Verde, Mozambique),
and the French (e.g., French Guiana, Haiti, Canada, Louisiana, Saint-
Louis-de-Sénégal). Each of these colonizing countries pushed their
agendas for expansion and to establish new economic strongholds
in vast, unexploited territories. Within this context, ports were vital
lynchpins in the colonial empire, the umbilical cord linking colony
to homeland, but also a risk since they typically represented the first
landing-site for imported diseases. However, new lands also came
with new people and new challenges, like new diseases. The hot and
humid tropics were particularly challenging from a colonial standpoint, lucrative in an economic sense, but also possessing new, ex-
otic and previously un encountered diseases; the colonizers were not
'seasoned' to these new diseases. Colonizers, of course, also imported
their own deadly new diseases to the virgin soil populations that they
colonized. The added element of disease dampened the lucrative pull
and promises of economic bounties in these new territories, and in
many cases, the colonizers questioned their long-term stability in
these new areas, often suggesting the removal of subjects when diseases became rampant. This section will examine some of the complex scenarios that emerged and caused strain between people and
place, and between colonizer and colonized.

The Dangers of Disease Exchange

Generally speaking, European colonial efforts, in the exploitation of
new lands, met its greatest challenges in infectious disease exposures
and exchanges. Not only could colonizers transmit new diseases to lo-

cal populations, and therefore devastate the potential labour force, the colonizers themselves could be affected by their own susceptibility to new diseases they encountered outside of Europe.[15] So-called 'tropical diseases,' foreign to the more temperate European climate, went a long way towards frustrating the enterprising and exploitative efforts of colonizers. Yellow fever, in particular, was one characteristic tropical infectious disease which came to be known as the "stranger's disease", since foreigners landing in an area where yellow fever was common were significantly more susceptible to the disease than locals. According to Tunali and Pritchett, for example, "...nineteenth century New Orleans had a reputation as the death capital of the United States" but in the worst epidemic of 1853, "foreign migrants accounted for more than 90% of yellow fever deaths although they represented less than one-half of the city's population."[16] It is generally understood today that the greater resistance of any local population coming into regular contact with a disease has to do with dynamics of exposure and immune system activity leading to greater resistance. But some earlier nineteenth century explanations centered on racial explanations, part icularly biological aspects underpinning perceived differences in human 'races', further opening the door to racism, scapegoating, and stigmatization[17] as continued exploration and ship-based travel increased the exposure to other cultures and climate conditions.

Even within one geographic area, regional differences in population-susceptibility to diseases with acquired immunity, such as yellow fever, were readily observed at the time of epidemic outbreaks. Take the United States, for example, where those living in the Southern states recognized the susceptibility of migrants from the northern states to yellow fever.[18] Pritchett and Tunali noted that a local New Orleans life insurance company was well aware of the greater susceptibility of migrants to the ravages of yellow fever and actually charged higher life insurance premiums to foreigners visiting the southern city in the summer months.[19]

Veracruz, New Mexico

Knaut highlights the paradox of the economic necessity of the port of Veracruz, New Mexico, in serving Spain's colonial interests in the Western hemisphere.[20] Veracruz was a central node in the connection between Spain and Mexico City (the capital of New Spain), and served as an important staging area in the local trade network, moving goods in and out of the region. New Spain's greatest asset, however, was also its greatest weakness since, as Knaut explains, Veracruz's "... notoriously vicious disease environment" not only damaged trade and commerce activities, but also foiled the best of military planning, since it was common for soldiers, who were brought down from the highlands to defend the port against possible British invasion, to be struck down by illness.[21]

Repeated waves of yellow fever outbreaks threatened vital functioning within Veracruz; the epidemic of 1802 was particularly devastating. A reputation for sickness within the port spread far and wide. During the epidemic of 1802, Knaut reported that the muleteers (mule-drivers), whose livelihood revolved around the movement of goods to and from the port, were hesitant to enter Veracruz in the throes of the epidemic:

> ...by summer's end, the heavy mortality brought trade in the port to a complete standstill, as muleteers from the highlands refused to descend to the disease-infested lowlands until the vomito season had passed...Muleteers, commercial agents, and others with business in the port often waited until nightfall before making the final descent in the hope that the lower temperatures of evening and early morning would ease their transition...and thereby lessen their chance of contracting the illness.[22]

Within this context, the health of Veracruz became a priority. Both military and commercial experts alike agreed that if public health conditions were not improved in the port, even the best economic and military investments would fail. Disease was the single most unruly element that had to be controlled if settlement in New Spain was to continue being successful.

Puerto Limón, Costa Rica

In an interesting case study, Adams examines current cultural and ethnic variation within Costa Rica from an historical standpoint, and factors in the possible effects of malaria for fostering this diversity.[23] Costa Rica was colonized by Spain in 1503, with Puerto Limón on the lowlands of the eastern coast serving as a suitable location for the agricultural undertakings which Spanish colonizers had planned for the area. After an intensive clearing of vegetation in and around the port, the land was ready for large-scale banana plantations; unbeknownst to the colonizers, however, the perfect ecological conditions for mosquito-borne infectious diseases emerged as an unforeseen byproduct. While Costa Rica's indigenous population suffered under the pressure of colonial conquest and the many new diseases imported with Spanish colonists, both the colonized and the colonizer alike fell victim, in large numbers, to new local fever diseases (most likely malaria). Puerto Limón was soon characterized as a dangerous place and Spaniards were thus encouraged to establish the main hub of economic activities further inland , deep in the highlands, and away from the deadly port. Adams suggests that the Spanish land-clearing practices, along with the introduction of the malaria Plasmodia in the blood of West African slaves/workers, and the importation of Anopheline mosquitoes in shipboard water supplies provided the combination of factors needed to establish endemic malaria in Costa Rica.

When intensive railroad-building projects were inaugurated in the 1800s, a wide net was cast in the search for labourers from China to Germany, Switzerland, and Italy. In the end, it was West Indian labourers, from Jamaica and other West Indian islands (many of whom were descendents of West African slaves), who filled this labour need. These new labourers to Costa Rica also found work on the banana plantations. Adams reports that West Indian immigrants disproportionately outnumbered any other group in and around the deadly environs of Puerto Limón. They were possibly protected from the ravages of malaria by biological adaptations (variants in red blood cell hemoglobins), carried through many generations but traced back to ethnic origins in West Africa. Today, in a country where evidence of Spanish colonization remains highly visible, Puerto Limón retains a remarkably unique character:

> In the 1960s, the residents of Puerto Limón held a parade in honor of Queen Elizabeth II's coronation and Jamaica's independence from British colonial rule. The local black population continues to speak an English-Spanish patois, despite the fact that Spanish is the official language of the country. Local radio stations broadcast more often in English than in Spanish; reggae music, not salsa or meringue, predominates the airwaves. [24]

Such local differences owe, in large part, to the fact that descendents of the West Indian immigrants to Costa Rica have maintained a stronger tie to Jamaica and other West Indian islands than the larger colonial Spanish influences. Taking only a modern-day snapshot of Costa Rica, this cultural diversity may be challenging to understand, but placed in historical context, and in particular the disease history of the country, as Adams does in this research, a broader understanding can be reached.

Saint-Louis-du-Sénégal, Africa

Ngalamulume argues that the combined observation of foreigners' susceptibility to yellow fever, the movement of European colonizers, and perspectives on disease causation pushed forward the agenda to socially distance the colonizers from the colonized. [25] In a study of the French colony of Saint-Louis-Du-Sénégal in Africa, Ngalamulume examines the miasmatic (localist, environmentalist) stance with re-

gards to epidemic outbreaks which served to open the door to allowing segregationist policies and the "pathologization of those classi-
fied as indigènes (working poor and underclass)" in urban colonial
Africa.²⁶ When the first yellow fever epidemic struck the city in 1867,
debate flared regarding the origins of the disease with both environmentalists (localists) and contagionists voicing their concerns. As
was the case in Veracruz, the environmentalists were quick to point
out the failings evident in Saint-Louis, particularly its predilection
for unhealthy pools of stagnant water caused by floods and torrential
rains and the naturally swampy environs of this port city. Prevailing
summer winds from the south and animal wastes (from slaughtering
and excrement) were other popular explanations for the generation
of miasmas. Since contagionists believed the disease had been imported into the city (Ngalamulume identifies communications with
other populations such as Sierra Leone, Gambia, and Portuguese
Guinea), it is not surprising that they recommended quarantine and
the establishment of sanitary cordons.

Overall, Ngalamulume contends that some combination of localist
and contagionist factors were considered by authorities in their dis-
cussions on how to explain, contain, and prevent this illness from
recurring in the community. Explanations favouring miasmatic origins, however, would have the greatest effect in straining civil relations within the diverse population comprising the city of Saint-Louis.
Those fearing miasmas as a source of disease were quick to point out
the unsanitary conditions in the city center, where both the marketplace and housing for the poor were located. This led to action. First,
the marketplace was relocated to the city outskirts, and then attention turned to the poor,

> ...authorities next targeted unsanitary housing, especially the shacks lo-
> cated in the city center that were seen as breeding grounds for the dis-
> ease...the policy [of forced removals] was justified by the inability of the
> indigènes to meet the requirements of the building codes in order to

prevent frequent fires during the cold season.[27]

The *indigènes* in Saint-Louis relied on a common and inexpensive building type – thatch-roofed houses – that were different from the types of homes which French colonizers occupied and therefore made them susceptible to denigration.

Class, Ethnicity, and Infectious Disease

In general, poor housing and slum areas in urban settings were easy and common targets for localists, perceived as they were to be hotbeds of disease and dangerous sources for miasmas. Yellow fever first ravaged the city of Rio de Janeiro, Brazil, in 1849-1850. When yellow fever reappeared again in the 1870s, the old debates regarding contagion and importation / infection, and miasmas reemerged. The focus of attention quickly turned to problems within the city, particularly "obstructions in the sewage system ...[and] the crowded and filthy dwellings inhabited by the poor" (known as cortiços or beehives), which were viewed literally as "cooking pots for the germs of yellow fever" and "overpopulated places with dirty stagnant waters and all sorts of damaging effluvia".[28] With the introduction of the Free Birth Law in 1871 in Brazil, and the shift from slavery to a free labour market, local authorities considered slum housing in Rio as a serious deterrent from attracting European immigrants who might have been considering the new labour opportunities opening up in Brazil. According to Chalhoub, "the destruction of the cortiços was necessary among other things because they were associated with immigrants dying of yellow fever, and because they gave the capital of the Empire – and also its main port of entry – the reputation of a pesthole, thus discouraging potential European immigrants from taking their chances in Brazil..."[29] Housing improvement, in this context, was only a part of the Brazilian government's redefinition of priorities following the Free Birth Law enactment. Since slaves and black labourers would no longer carry the weight of the economy, attention paid to the diseases that disproportionately affected these groups (notably cholera) would soon fall second to diseases (yellow fever) that disproportionately affected European immigrant workers. Here, Chalhoub argues, we can begin to appreciate how the political and social agendas of governments can influence why certain diseases get targeted for action and others do not.

Housing issues, particularly those associated with homes in economically-depressed areas, continue to receive the attention of those interested in public health today. Changes in building practices have introduced new concerns that must be considered. McMichael, for example, highlights the case of infectious disease outbreaks in high-rise housing, a situation which came to light with the outbreak of SARS in Hong Kong. [30] High-rises represent a type of high-density living, and are typically found in urban settings where land opportunities are notably restricted. In addition to a large number of people in one place, everyone typically moves in and out of the same access points, and share common elevators. Like office buildings and other institutional settings, high-rise occupants are typically connected via the same ventilation and heating systems, which increases the risk of air-borne diseases. In today's world, it is well understood that not only class differences, but also the limited availability of land in highly developed areas, can have an influence on diversity in housing types.

The effects of interactions between humans, housing, and vectors on the spread of infectious disease have been observed with respect to a number of epidemics besides yellow fever. The entry of bubonic plague into human populations, for example, was typically accompanied by the work of fleas (*Pulex irritans*) and black rats (*Rattus rattus*). Benedictow summarizes mortality differentials in several European settlements in the plague's peak.[31] As a case in point, in a small northern German town, it was generally observed that "upper-class families living in stone or brick-built houses with tile roofs and stone or plaster floors...were spared, while the lower classes living in dilapidated wooden houses...suffered" disproportionately from plague-related mortality, presumably because rats (and, therefore, the fleas they carried) had easier access to the houses of the poor.[32] Meanwhile, in the same town, more differences were noted. The noise and disturbance created by smiths (e.g., blacksmiths) at work kept rats away, while bakers, butchers, and linen-weavers (using linseed) attracted rats to their residences and suffered more deaths upon the introduction of the plague. Just the very nature of a town layout could influence the distribution of plague-carrying rats since, as McCormick has noted, rats do not like to cross streets.[33]

Last Thoughts

There are many features of human populations today that are changing and influencing interactions between humans and microbes more generally. With respect to infectious diseases, McMichael lists several factors that are creating new opportunities for microbial activities in human populations, including: the mobility of human populations andever-expanding long-distance trade networks, growing cities complete with slums, which "become highways for microbial traffic", and vulnerability-inducing poverty.[34] There are also behavioural factors such as, risky sexual practices, illicit drug-injecting, intensified food production, and modern medical technology.[35] As a case in point, McMichael highlights hepatitis C as an example of an infectious disease that is emerging due, in large part, to "social-technological change," notably "the advent of illicit intravenous drug use and...medical transfusion."[36] The history of medical practices, such as blood transfusions, takes us only as far back as the 20th century when techniques of blood typing, donor-recipient matching, and blood banks were being perfected and established. Our understanding of the important life-saving aspects of this innovation in medical technology has been counterbalanced by the observation that, without suitable screening practices, blood can also serve as an important vehicle for the transmission of infectious disease.

The dynamics inherent in today's increasingly globalized world have influenced the behaviour of several infectious diseases that were of historic importance, and which continue to plague human populations today. McMichael details the cholera pandemics, seven in all, the first of which emerged out of Asia in 1817. With the evolution of maritime technology, by "...the early 1830s, the faster-traveling steamboats enabled cholera to cross the Atlantic" for the first time.[37] The current cholera pandemic, caused by a relatively milder El Tor strain, began in 1961 and is credited as "the longest pandemic to date," achieving a deep global spread because of:

> ...the greatly-increased volume of human movement between continents, the greater rapidity and distance of modern shipping-based trade, the escalation in nutrient enrichment of coastal and estuarine waters by phosphates and nitrates in run-off wastewater, and the proliferation of urban slums without access to safe drinking water.[38]

Though the El Tor strain is not as virulent as the *Vibrio cholera* strains involved in previous pandemics, it is the human influence, and not so much the biology of the microbe itself, that is believed to be largely responsible for the long-term endurance of the current pandemic.

Chapter Five Endnotes:

[1]Judge Chambers 24th November 1887.

[2]As quoted in Frendo, H. (1988) The British Colonial Experience 1800-1964. The Impact on Maltese Society. Edited by Mallia-Milanes, V. Amsterdam: Mireva Publication. p. 198.

[3]TRIAY

[4]Finlayson, T.J. (1997) The Press in Gibraltar in the Nineteenth Century. Gibtel Gibraltar Heritage Journal. Volume 4 page 91-108. According to Finlayson (1997:91), "the Gibraltar Chronicle started publication in 1801. ...[when]... General O'Hara recommended the Committee of the Garrison Library to purchase a set of types and printing press for the dissemination in Spain of the true facts relative to the Egyptian campaign. French bulletins in that country had for some time been giving distorted accounts of the events in Egypt."

[5]Sir Robert Wilson, Governor of Gibraltar, to the Right Honourable Earl Grey, Secretary of State for the Colonies. Confidential. 29th April, 1848 (GGA).

[6]CO 91/ 342 July 18th, 1877. Napier of Mag.... to the Earl of Caravan.

[7]Frendo, H. (1988) The British Colonial Experience 1800-1964. The Impact on Maltese Society. Edited by Mallia-Milanes, V. Amsterdam: Mireva Publication. p. 198.

[8]Gibraltar and its Sieges 1900. p. 122.

[9]Field 1888, 30.

[10]CO 91/309 25th June 1870 Solly Flood to R.S. Baynes.

[11]CO 91/309 25th June 1870 Solly Flood to R.S. Baynes (and Howes 1950, 189).

[12]Kelaart, EF (1846) Flora Calpenesis Contributions to the Botany and Topography of Gibraltar and its Neighbourhood. London: John van Voorst, 1 Paternoster-Row. p. 52.

[13]Sawchuk, LA (1992) Historical Intervention, Tradition, and Change: A Study of the Age of Marriage in Gibraltar, 1909-1983. Journal of Family History 17: 69-94.

[14]Originally, Jamaica was a Spanish colony and then drawn into the British Empire.

[15]See, for example, Peard 1997.

[16]Tunali and Pritchett 1997, 3.

[17]See Peard, 1997.

[18]Humphreys 1992; Knaut 1997.

[19]Pritchett and Tunali 1995.

[20]Knaut 1997.

[21]Knaut 1997, 621.
[22]Knaut 1997, 630-631.
[23]Adams 1996.
[24]Adams 1996, 84.
[25]Ngalamulume 2004.
[26]Ngalamulume 2004, 185.
[27]Ngalamulume 2004, 190.
[28]Chalhoub 1993, 456-457.
[29]Chalhoub 1993, 438; see also Peard 1997.
[30]McMichael 2004.
[31]Benedictow 1987.
[32]Benedictow 1987, 425.
[33]McCormick 2003.
[34]McMichael 2004, 1050.
[35]McMichael 2004, 1050.
[36]McMichael 2004, 1051.
[37]McMichael 2004.
[38]McMichael 2004, 1050.

References Cited

Manuscript Sources

William Thornton, Gibraltar Fever Diary, 1828. Archives and Manuscripts: MS 7816/2. Wellcome Library, London.

CO - Colonial Office Original Correspondence (Public Record Office, London).

WO - War Office Original Correspondence (Public Record Office, London).

GGA - Colonial Original Correspondence (Gibraltar Government Archives, Gibraltar).

ADM - Army Department Medical (Public Record Office, London).

Published Primary Sources:

Printed Material

Amiel, R. Surgeon, 12th Regiment, resident for many years in Gibraltar, and a witness of the epidemics of 1813, 1814 and 1828. Answers to Queries from the Army Medical Board, on the Epidemic at Gibraltar.

Bland, Lieutenant-General 1752. An Account of Lieutenant General Bland's Conduct ... .

Douglas Chester, W.M. 1877 Report on the Quarantine Practice in force at Gibraltar to Charles Lennox Peel, Clerk of the Council.

Fraser, W.W. A Letter, &c. &c. Gibraltar 24th of August, 1822.

Newspapers
Gibraltar Chronicle (Gibraltar)

Reports and Official Publications
Gibraltar Blue Books
Census of Gibraltar - Published and unpublished nominative census material.

Published Secondary Sources

Abel, Christopher 1995 External Philanthropy and Domestic Change in Colombian Health Care: The Role of the Rockefeller Foundation, ca. 1920-1950. The Hispanic American Historical Review 75: 339-376.

Adams, David P. 1996 Malaria, Labor, and Population Distribution in Costa Rica: A Biohistorical Perspective. Journal of Interdisciplinary History 27:75-85.

Alderson, M.R. 1985 Season and Mortality. Health Trends 17: 87-96

Aldrich, R. and J.Connell 1998 The Last Colonies. Cambridge University Press, Cambridge.

Allison, Anthony C. 1954 Protection Afforded by Sickle Cell Trait Against Malarial Infection. British Medical Journal 1:290-294

Anonymous 1827/28 Nicholas Chervin's Researches on the Nature of Yellow Fever. Lancet 2: 679.

Anonymous Historical Sketch of the Epidemic Yellow Fever which prevailed at Gibraltar in the Autumn of 1828. Lancet 1829/30. Page 325-330.

Anonymous Gibraltar and its Sieges with a Description of Its Natural Features. 1900 Thomas Nelson and Sons, London.

Anonymous 1830 The Soldier's Cemetery at Gibraltar. United Service Magazine. P. 720

Anonymous 1830 Letters From Gibraltar No. III. April 29th, 1830 Letters No IV. June 1, 1830. Page 427.

Anton, J. 1998 Description of Gibraltar in the 1820s. Reprinted in the Gibraltar Heritage Journal. No. 5: 77-102. (From Anton, J. Retrospect of a Military Life. Edinburgh, 1841).

Arnold, David 1993 Colonizing the Body. University of California Press, Berkley.

Augustin, G. 1909 History of Yellow Fever. New Orleans, Searcy & Pfaff.

Barrett, F.A. 2000 Disease and Geography. The History of An Idea. Atkinson College, Department of Geography

Barrett, R., Kuzawa, C.W., McDade, T., & Armelagos, G. 1998 Emerging and re-emerging infectious diseases: the third epidemiologic transition. Annual Review of Anthropology, 27, 247-71.

Barry, K.T.S. 1830 On the Sanitary Management of the Gibraltar Epidemic Fever. Thomas Wilson, London.

Bayly, Colonel. 1896. Diary of Colonel Bayly, 12th Regiment, 1796-1830. London Army and Navy Cooperative Society Ltd.

Benedict, Carol 1996 Bubonic Plague in Nineteenth-Century China. Stanford, California: Stanford University Press.

Benedictow, O.J. 1987 Morbidity in Historical Plague Epidemics. Population Studies 41:401-431.

Benady, S. 1994 Civil Hospital and Epidemics in Gibraltar. Gibraltar Books Ltd., Gibraltar.

Bigelow, A. 1831 Travels in Malta and Sicily with Sketches of Gibraltar in 1827. Carter, Hendee and Babcock, Boston.

Bouckaert, A. 1989 Crisis Mortality: extinction and near extinction of human populations. In: Differential Mortality: Methodological Issues and Biosocial Factors, ed. L. Rudicka, G. Wunsch and P. Kane. Pp. 217-30. Oxford, Clarendon Press.

Burke, S.D.A. and L.A. Sawchuk. 2001 Alien Encounters: Overcrowding, the Jus soli, and Reproductive Politics in 19th Century Gibraltar. The History of the Family: An International Quarterly 6: 1-31.

Carolina, M. & Gustavo, L. 2003 Epidemiological transition: Model or illusion? A look at the problem of health in Mexico. Social Science and Medicine, 57, 539-550.

Carrigan, J.A. 1994 The Saffron Scourge: A History of Yellow Fever in Louisiana, 1796-1905. Lafayette, La: Center for Louisiana Studies, University of South western Louisiana.

Cartwright, Frederick 1972 Disease and History. New York: Dorset Press.

Caruana, C. 1989 The Rock Under A Cloud. Silent Books, U.K.

Chalhoub, Sidney 1993 The Politics of Disease Control: Yellow Fever and Race in Nineteenth Century Rio de Janeiro. Journal of Latin American Studies 25: 441-463.

Cherry, S. 1980 The Hospitals and Population Growth: Part I and Part II. The Voluntary General Hospitals, Mortality and Local Populations in the English Provinces in the Eighteenth and Nineteenth Centuries. Population Studies 34: 59-75; 251-265.

Chervin, M.M., Louis et Trousseau, membres de la commission francaise envoyée a Gibraltar pour observer l'épidémie de 1828: Documens recuellis par ... et par M. le Dr. Barry, médecin des armées anglaises, 2 volumes. Paris: Imprimerie royale, 1830.

Christophers, S.R. 1960 Aedea aegypti. The life History of the Yellow Fever mosquito, Bionomics and Structure. Cambridge, Cambridge University press 1960.

Clarke, J. 1831/32 Observations on the Influence of Fear in Predisposing to Disease. Lancet 1: 914-15.

Coleman, W. 1987 Yellow Fever in the North: The Methods of Early Epidemiology. University of Wisconsin Press, Madison.

Coles, N. 1986 Sinners in the Hands of an Angry Utilitarian. J.P. Kay Shutterworth, The Moral and Physical Condition on the Working Classes in Manchester (1832). Bulletin of Research on the Humanities.

Cook, I., & Dummer, T. 2004 Changing health in China: re-evaluating the epidemiological transition model. Health Policy, 67, 329-343.

Cooper, F. and A. Stoler 1989. Tensions of empire: colonial control and visions of rule. American ethnologist 16: 609-621.

Cueto, Marcos 1992 Sanitation from Above: Yellow Fever and Foreign Intervention in Peru, 1919-1922. The Hispanic American Historical Review 72: 1-22.

Curtin, P.D. 1989 Death by Migration. Cambridge University Press, New York.

Diaz, H.F. and G.J. McCabe 1999 A possible connection between the 1878 yellow fever epidemic in the southern United States and the 1877-78 El Nino episode. Bulletin of American Meteorological Society 80: 21-28.

Dictionary of National Biography 1908 Sir Leslie Stephen & Sir Sidney Lee. Oxford University Press, Oxford.

Dobson, M.J. 1989 Mortality gradients and disease exchanges: comparisons from old England and colonial America. Social History Medicine 2: 259-297.

Dwight, T. 1824 A Tour in Italy in the Year 1821 with a Description of Gibraltar.

By an American. Abraham Paw, New York.

Edwards, D.O. 1830 The Gibraltar Fever. Westminster Hospital. May 18th 1830. To the Editor of the Lancet.

Ellis, J.H. 1992 Yellow Fever & Public Health in the New South. University of Kentucky Press, Lexington, Kentucky.

Eritja, Roger, Raul Escosa, Javier Lucientes, Eduard Marques, Ricardo Molina, David Roiz, and Santiago Ruiz 2005 Worldwide invasion of vector mosquitoes: present European distribution and challenges for Spain. Biological Invasions 7: 87-97.

Evans, R.J. 1987 Death in Hamburg. Society and Politics in the Cholera Years 1830 -1910. Clarendon Press, Oxford.

Garcia-Moro, C., Hernandez, M., Moral, P., & Gonzalez-Martin, A. 2000 Epidemiological transition in Easter Island (1914-1996). American Journal of Human Biology, 12, 371-381.

Gaylin, D., & Kates, J. 1997 Refocusing the Lens: Epidemiological Transition Theory, Mortality Differentials, and the AIDS Pandemic. Social Science and Medicine, 44, 609-621.

Goodman, A.H. and T.L. Leatherman 1998 Building a New Biocultural Synthesis. University of Michigan Press, Ann Arbor.

Finlayson, T.J. 1996 Stories From the Rock. Aquila Services, Ltd., Gibraltar.

Finlayson, T.J. 1997 The Press in Gibraltar in the Nineteenth Century. Gibtel Gibraltar Heritage Journal. Volume 4 p. 91-108.

Finlayson, T.J. 2001 The Disputed Land. Unpublished Document. Gibraltar Archives.

Richard Ford. 1855 Gatherings from Spain (Everyman edition). Centaur, London.

Fox, D.M. 1989 The History of Responses to Epidemic Disease in the United States since the 18th Century. The Mount Sinai Journal of Medicine 56: 223-229.

Fraser, Hugh 1830 Review of the Facts and Arguments Brought Forward by Dr. Barry, at the Royal College of Physicians, Relative to the Late Epidemic Fever in the Fortress of Gibraltar. By Hugh Fraser, Esq. Surgeon of the Civil Hospital, and late Assistant Surgeon, 12th Regiment. Medico-Chirurgical Review n.s. 13 August 1830, 337-350.

Gilbard, Major G. J. 1883 Gibraltar Directory and Guidebook. Republished by Gibraltar Books Ltd, Grendon. 1992.

Geggus, D. 1979 Yellow Fever in the 1790s: The British Army in Occupied Saint Domingue. Medical History 23: 38-58.

Goodman, A.H. and T.L. Leatherman 1998 Building a New Biocultural Synthesis. University of Michigan Press, Ann Arbour.

Gubler, Duane J. 2002 The Global Emergence/Resurgence of Arboviral Diseases as Public Health Problems. Archives of Medical Research 33: 330-342.

Gubler, Duane J. 2004 The Changing Epidemiology of Yellow Fever and Dengue, 1900 to 2003: Full Circle? Comparative Immunology, Microbiology & Infectious Diseases 27: 319-330.

Hardy, Anne 1993 The Epidemic Streets: Infectious Disease and the Rise of Preventive Medicine, 1856-1900. Oxford: Clarendon Press.

Hardy, Anne 1993 Cholera, Quarantine and the English Preventive System, 1850-1895. Medical History 37:250-269.

Harrington, Laura C., John D. Edman, and Thomas W. Scott 2001 Why Do Female Aedes aegypti (Diptera: Culicidae) Feed Preferentially and Frequently on Human Blood? Journal of Medical Entomology 38: 411-422.

Hennen, J. 1830 Sketches of the Medical Topography of the Mediterranean comprising an account of Gibraltar, the Ionian Islands, and Malta; to which is prefixed, A Sketch of a Plan for Memoirs on Medical Topography. Thomas and George Underwood, Fleet Street, London.

Herring, D.A. and A.C. Swedlund (Editors) 2003 Human Biology in the Archives. Cambridge University Press, Cambridge.

Hills, G. 1974 Rock of Contention: A History of Gibraltar. Robert Hale and Company, London.

Howard-Jones, N. 1972 Cholera Therapy in the Nineteenth Century. Journal of History of Medicine and Allied Sciences 27:373-395.

Howes, H.W. 1950 The Gibraltarian. The origin and development of the population of Gibraltar from 1704. City Press, Colombo (Ceylon).

Humphreys, M. 1992 Yellow Fever and the South. Rutgers University Press, New Jersey.

Humphreys, M. 1997 Appendix II: Yellow Fever Since 1793: History and Historiography. In: A Melancholy Scene of Devastation. Edited by Estes, J.W. and B.G. Smith. Science History Publications, Philadelphia. pp. 183-198.

Jackson, Sir W.G.F 1987 The Rock of the Gibraltarians: A History of Gibraltar. Associated University Press, London.

Jackson, Fatimah L.C. 2000 Human Adaptations to Infectious Disease. In: Human Biology: An Evolutionary and Biocultural Perspective (Sara Stinson, Barry Bogin, Rebecca Huss-Ashmore, and Dennis O'Rourke, Eds.) New York, NY: Wiley-Liss, Inc.

Kelaart, E.F. 1846 Flora Calpensis Contributions to the Botany and Topography of Gibraltar and its Neighbourhood. John van Voorst, 1, Paternoster-Row, London.

Knaut, Andrew L. 1997 Yellow Fever and the Late Colonial Public Health Response in the Port of Veracruz. The Hispanic American Historical Review 77: 619-644.

Kopperman, Paul E. 2004 "Venerate the Lancet": Benjamin Rush's Yellow Fever Therapy in Context. Bulletin of the History of Medicine 78: 539-574.

Lawrance, C. 1994 The History of the old Naval Hospital, Gibraltar, 1741 to 1922. Great Britain, Christine Lawrance.

Lee, Debbie 1998 Yellow Fever and the Slave Trade: Coleridge's The Rime of the Ancient Mariner. English Literary History 65: 675-700.

Lim, Sue, Tom Closson, Gillian Howard, and Michael Gardam 2004 Collateral Damage: the unforeseen effects of emergency outbreak policies. Lancet 697-703.

Louis, P.C.A. 1839 Anatomical, Pathological and Therapeutic Researches on the Yellow Fever of Gibraltar in 1828. Boston.

Löwy, Ilana 1997 Epidemiology, Immunology, and Yellow Fever: The Rockefeller Foundation in Brazil, 1923-1939. Journal of the History of Biology 30: 397-417.

McGrew, R.E. 1962 The First Russian Epidemic: Themes and Opportunities. Bulletin of the History of Medicine 36: 220-244.

McNeil, W.H. 1976 Plagues and Peoples. Anchor Press, New York.

Marks, S. 1997 What is Colonial about Colonial Medicine? And What has Happened to Imperialism and Health? Social History of Medicine 10: 205-219.

Martin, R.M. 1837 History of the British Possessions in the Mediterranean: Comprising Gibraltar, Malta, Gozo, and the Ionian Islands. Whittaker & Co., Ave Maria Lane, London.

Mather, J. R. 1974 Climatology: Fundamentals and Applications. McGraw-Hill Book., Co., New York.

McCormick, Michael 2003 Rats, Communication, and Plague: Toward an Ecological History. Journal of Interdisciplinary History 34:1-25.

McKeown, Thomas 1976 The Modern Rise of Population. New York: Academic Press.

McMichael, A.J. 2004 Environmental and social influences on emerging infectious diseases: past, present and future. Phil. Trans. R. Soc. Lond. B 359: 1049-1058.

Monath, T.P. 1989 Yellow Fever In: Monath, T.P. ed. The arboviruses: ecology and epidemiology. Vol. V. CRC Press, Boca Raton, 139-231.

Moncayo, Abelardo C., Zoraida Fernandez, Diana Ortiz, Mawlouth Diallo, Amadou Sall, Sammie Hartman, C. Todd Davis, Lark Coffey, Christian C. Mathiot, Robert B. Tesh, and Scott C. Weaver 2004 Dengue Emergence and Adaptation to Peridomestic Mosquitoes. Emerging Infectious Diseases 10: 1790-1796.

Morris, R.J. 1976 Cholera 1832. Croon Helm, London.

Ngalamulume, Kalala 2004 Keeping the City Totally Clean: Yellow Fever and the Politics of Prevention in Colonial Saint-Louis-du-Sénégal, 1850-1914. Journal of African History 45: 183-202.

Palloni, A. 1990 Assessing the Levels and Impact of Mortality in Crisis Situations. In: Measurement and Analysis of Mortality (J. Vallin, S. D'Souza, and A. Palloni, eds.) Oxford: Clarendon Press. Pp. 194-228.

Patterson, K.D. 1992 Yellow Fever Epidemics and Mortality in the United States, 1693-1905. Social Science and Medicine 34: 855-865.

Peard, Julyan G. 1997 Tropical Disorders and the Forging of a Brazilian Medical Identity, 1860-1890. The Hispanic American Historical Review 77: 1-44

Pelling, M. 1978 Cholera, Fever and English Medicine, 1825-1865. Oxford University Press, Oxford.

Pelling, M. 1993 Contagion/Germ Theory Specificity. In: Companion Encyclopaedia of the History of Medicine. W.F. Bynum and R. Porter Editors. Routledge, London. Pp. 309-333.

Petersen, J.L. 1977 Behavior differences in two subspecies of Aedes aegypti (L.) (Diptera: Culicidae) in East Africa. Ph.D. dissertation. University of Notre Dame, Notre Dame, IN.

Preston, R.A. 1946 Gibraltar, Colony and Fortress. Canadian Historical Review 27: 402-423.

Pritchett, J.B. and I. Tunali 1995 Strangers' Disease: Determinants of yellow fever mortality during the New Orleans epidemic of 1853. Exp. Econ. Hist. 32: 517-39.

Pym, W. 1838 Observations upon Bulam, Vomito-Negro or Yellow Fever. John Churchill, London.

Robertson, Rev. W. 1841 A Residence at Gibraltar and a Visit to the Peninsula in the Summer and Autumn of 1841. A. Fullarton & Co., Edinburgh and London.

Rose, E.P.F. and M.S. Rosenbaum 1991 A Field Guide to the Geology of Gibraltar. Gibraltar Museum, Gibraltar.

Rosenburg, C.E. 1962 The Cholera Years: The United States in 1832, 1849 and 1866. University of Chicago Press, Chicago.

Rosenburg, C.E. 1966 Cholera in Nineteenth-Century Europe: A Tool for Social and Economic Analysis. Comparative Studies in Society and History. 8: 452-463.

Rousey, Dennis C. 1985 Yellow Fever and Black Policemen in Memphis: A Post-Reconstruction Anomaly. The Journal of Southern History 51: 357-374.

Rule, Rev. W.H. 1844 Memoir of a Mission to Gibraltar and Spain, with collateral notices. London, John Mason.

Sanguinetti, M.L. 1993 Gibraltar's Architecture. Journal of the Friends of Gibraltar Heritage Society 1: 5-10.

Sayer, F. 1865 The History of Gibraltar and Its Political Relation to Events in Europe. 2nd Ed. Chapman and Hall, London.

Sawchuk, L.A. 1996 Rainfall, Patio Living, and Crisis Mortality in a Scale-Scale Society: The Benefits of a Tradition of Scarcity. Current Anthropology 37: 863-867.

Sawchuk, L.A., S.D.A. Burke, and J. Padiak. 2002 A Matter of Privilege: Infant Mortality in the Garrison Town of Gibraltar, 1870-1899. Journal of Family History (special issue on the theme of The Military and the Family) 27: 399-429.

Seale, Clive. 2000 Changing patterns of death and dying. Social Science and Medicine, 51, 917-930.

Scott, T.W., E. Chow, E. Strickman, P. Kittayapong, R.A. Wirtz, L.H. Lorenz, and J.D. Edman 1993 Blood feeding pattersn of Aedes aegypti (Diptera: Culicidae) during a single gonotrophic cycle using a histological technique. Journal of Medical Entomology 30: 922-927.

Scott, T.W., A.C. Morrison, L.H. Lorenz, G.G. Clark, D. Strickman, P. Kittay apong, H. Zhou, and J.D. Edman 2000 Longitudinal studies of Aedes aegypti (Diptera: Culicidae) in Thailand and Puerto Rico: population dynamics. Journal of Medical Entomology 37:77-88.

Slosek, Jean 1986 Aedes aegypti Mosquitoes in the Americas: A Review of Their Interactions with the Human Population. Social Science and Medicine 23:249-257.

Smith, C.E. and M.E. Gibson 1986 Yellow Fever in South Wales, 1865. Medical History 30: 322-340.

Smith, B.G. 1997 Comment: Disease and Community. In: A Melancholy Scene of Devastation. Edited by Estes, J.W. and B.G. Smith. Science History Publications, Philadelphia.

Smith, C.E. Gordon and Mary E. Gibson 1986 Yellow Fever in South Wales, 1865. Medical History 30:322-340.

Snowden, F.M. 1995 Naples in the Time of Cholera, 1884-1911. Cambridge University Press, Cambridge.

Stewart, J.D. 1967 Gibraltar, the Keystone. Murray, London.

Svanborg-Eden, Catharina and Bruce R. Levin 1990 Infectious Disease and Natural Selection in Human Populations: A Critical Reexamination. In: Disease in Populations in Transition: Anthropological and Epidemiological Perspectives (Alan C. Swedlund and George J. Armelagos, Eds.) New York: Bergin and Garvey.

Szreter, Simon 1988 The Importance of Social Intervention in Britain's Mortality Decline c.1850-1914: a Re-interpretation of the Role of Public Health. Social History of Medicine 1:1-37.

Tellis, W. 1997 Application of a Case Study Methodology. The Qualitative Report 3. September.

Tunali, Insan and Jonathan B. Pritchett 1997 Cox Regression with Alternative Concepts of Waiting Time: The New Orleans Yellow Fever Epidemic of 1853. Journal of Applied Econometrics 12: 1-25.

Vandervelde, V. D. and R.J.M. Garcia 1994 Gibraltar Quarantine and Disinfection of Mail. Malcom Beresford Montgomery, Southampton.

Vasconcelos, Pedro F.C., Juliet E. Bryant, Amelia P.A. Travassos da Rosa, Robert B. Tesh, Sueli G. Rodrigues, and Alan D.T. Barrett 2004 Genetic Divergence and Dispersal of Yellow Fever Virus, Brazil. Emerging Infectious Diseases 10: 1578-1584.

Walsh, T. 1803 Journal in the Late Campaign in Egypt. Including descriptions of that country and of Gibraltar, Minorca, Malta, Minorca, and Macri. T. Cadell and W. Davies in the Strand, London.

Waters, W.F. 2001 Globalization, socioeconomic restructuring, and community health. Journal of Community Health, 26, 79-92

Watts, S.J. 1997 Epidemics and History: disease, power and imperialism. Yale University Press, New Haven.

Weiss, Robin A. and Anthony J. McMichael 2004 Social and Environmental Risk Factors in the Emergence of Infectious Diseases. Nature Medicine 10:S70-S76.

Wills, C. 1996 Yellow Fever Black Goddess. Helix Books, Reading, Massachusetts.

Wilson, P. 1829/30. Historical Sketch of the Epidemic Yellow Fever which prevailed at Gibraltar in the Autumn of 1828. Lancet Page 325-330.

Worth Estes, J. and B.G. Smith 1997 A Melancholy Scene of Devastation. Edited by. Science History Publications, Philadelphia.

Yale, Rev. R. n.d. A Story in Stone being a History of Kings Chapel.

Yin, R. 1993. Applications of case study research. Newbury Park, CA: Sage Publishing.

Index

N

O

P

Q

R

S

Biographies

Sawchuk, L.A.
Larry is an Associate Professor at the University of Toronto at Scarborough. He has worked in Gibraltar since 1974 studying aspects of health of the Gibraltarians.

Benady, S.G.
Sam has studied medicine in England, and worked in England and Israel before returning to Gibraltar in 1980. Sam Benady retired as single-handed Consultant Paediatrician to the Gibraltar Health Authority in 2002, after more than 22 years during which he set up a paediatric service on the Rock almost from scratch. During his tenure, he saw the perinatal mortality in Gibraltar fall from over 23 per 1000 to less than 8 per 1000.

He has published Civil Hospital and Epidemics in Gibraltar (1994), as well as many articles on aspects of the history of Gibraltar, and short stories Sherlock Holmes in Gibraltar (1990). Forthcoming books are The Keys of the City (a novel about medieval Gibraltar) and a life of Sir George Don (Lieutenant Governor of Gibraltar from 1814 to 1831). He is a member of the Board of the Gibraltar Heritage Trust, and of the Committee of the Gibraltar Garrison Library. He has collaborated with his present co-authors in the past.

Burke, S.D.A.
Stacie is an Assistant Professor in the Department of Anthropology, University of Manitoba. Her current research interests include the impact of infectious diseases on communities and families, gender and health, and reproductive behaviour and family formation. With a grant from the Social Sciences and Humanities Research Council of Canada, Burke and Sawchuk are now researching "Tuberculosis and the Family in Ontario: 1900-1950".